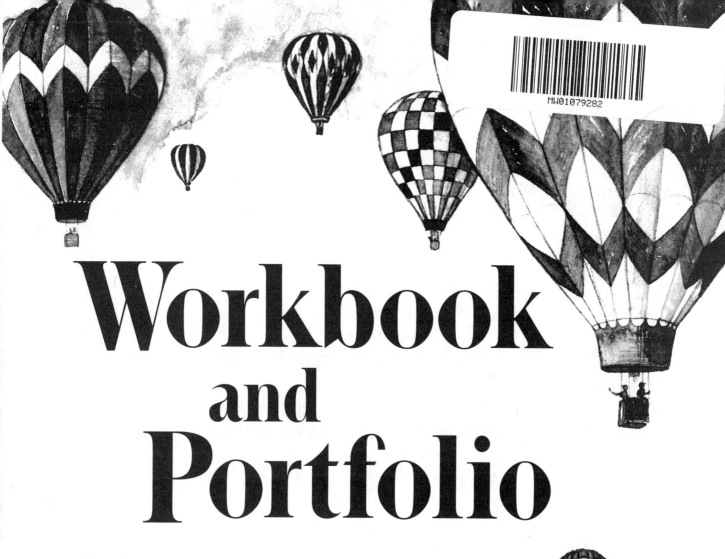

Workbook and Portfolio

For the text:

Career Choices

A Guide for Teens and Young Adults:
Who Am I?
What Do I Want?
How Do I Get It?

by Mindy Bingham and Sandy Stryker

illustrated by Itoko Maeno, Janice Blair and Diana Lackner

Copyright ©1990 by Melinda Bingham and Sandy Stryker

ISBN 1-878787-03-9

Published by Academic Innovations
3463 State Street, Suite 267A
Santa Barbara, California 93105
(805) 967-8015   FAX (805) 967-4357

Manufactured in the United States of America   20 19 18 17 16 15 14 13 12 11

CONTENTS

How to Use this Workbook

All the written exercises in *Career Choices* along with their directions are reprinted in this *Workbook*.

To find a particular exercise —

- First note the chapter you are reading in *Career Choices*.
- Then turn to the table of contents on page 2 of this *Workbook* to find the page on which the chapter begins.
- In the margins of this *Workbook* are boxes with numbers. These correspond to the page in *Career Choices* on which you'll find the particular exercise. In most cases the exercise will look exactly as it does in *Career Choices*.

While the directions to the exercise are included in this *Workbook*, the explanations and examples are not. To fully understand the activity you will need to read the text in *Career Choices* preceding the exercise.

In addition, when the directions or an exercise note a page number for reference or resource, this citation corresponds to the page number in *Career Choices*, so be sure to look these up in *Career Choices*, not in the *Workbook*.

At the beginning of each chapter of the *Workbook* are a list of vocabulary words found in that chapter in *Career Choices*. It should be helpful to review these words and write their definitions before reading the chapter. Then once you come across these words, they will have more meaning for you.

"Know Thyself" is one of the most challenging yet important tasks of our lives. People who know who they are and what they want have a better chance of figuring out how to achieve their own form of success and, ultimately, happiness and personal contentment. Your *Workbook* should be a record of this important adventure at this critical time in your development. Keep it along with other important documents and review it over the course of your life. Who knows, someday you may wish to share it with another young person in your life.

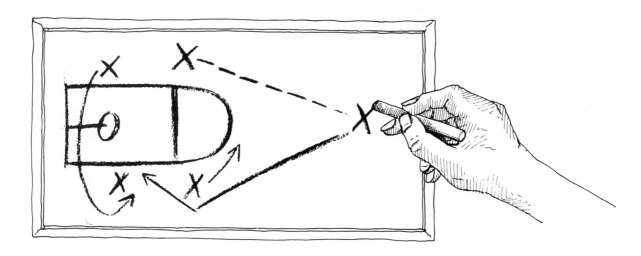

Chapter 1

Vocabulary List

elaborate _____

gamut _____

vision _____

realization _____

frustration _____

security _____

discrimination _____

achievement _____

fanatic _____

excess _____

flaunt _____

prima donna _____

integrity _____

humility _____

intuition _____

impulsive _____

procrastination _____

compliant _____

rational _____

interchangeable _____

VISION + ENERGY = SUCCESS

What do you think are the *real* stories behind the successful people we talked about on the preceding pages? For the following exercises, write a statement that you feel might reflect his or her vision. Then list some actions they may have taken to realize their goal.

Complete charts for the following individuals.

Sally Ride

Vision: _____

Actions in school: _____

Actions at work: _____

Oprah Winfrey

Vision: _____

Actions in school: _____

Actions at work: _____

Bill Clinton

Vision: _____

Actions in school: _____

Actions at work: _____

Your Portfolio

There are a number of activities in this book you will want to include in your portfolio once you have completed them. The information gathered will be vital to the success of your career and life planning process over the next few years. So that this information is readily available when meeting with school counselors, career advisors and mentors, as well as when preparing for job interviews, once you have completed your work in this book, Academic Innovations grants permission to the consumers of this workbook the right to photocopy the following **completed** workbook pages for inclusion into their personal portfolio.

Pages: 6, 11, 28, 42, 62, 83, 87, 112, 113, 121, 122, 123, 124.

Envisioning Your Future

What about you? Do you have a vision for your own future? You need to begin imagining one if you don't. It's an important first step. Once you have a vision, you start expecting to realize it. What you *expect* for yourself tends to become what you *get*. So imagine a *positive* future for yourself.

Sit quietly, close your eyes, and imagine your ideal career. What kind of setting are you in? What tasks are you performing? Are you working alone or with others? How do you feel about yourself? Describe your vision in as much detail as possible.

_____

_____

_____

_____

_____

_____

_____

_____

_____

_____

Everybody Works

Whether you currently earn money from a job or not, you are a worker. You are probably a student. Chances are, you do chores at home. Perhaps you are an athlete or a musician, a computer whiz or a video fanatic, a cook or a gardener. For the purpose of this exercise, consider all your studies, tasks, and hobbies as work.

Think about a typical "working day," one in which you spent time on most of your "jobs." List the tasks and activities you performed below. Make your list as complete as you can.

_____

_____

_____

Based on that list, how would you define your jobs? Write your titles on the following lines.

I am a _____

_____

_____

What would be your accomplishments at the end of the day (an English paper, a clean room, a solved problem, and so on)? List them below.

_____

_____

_____

Which accomplishments are most satisfying? _____

_____

How do they make you feel about yourself? _____

_____

Do your feelings relate to any of the reasons people work listed on the previous page? Which ones?

_____

_____

Defining Success

What does success mean to you? What would make you feel that you are a successful human being? In addition to thinking about what you do, contemplate the type of person you want to be.

Other people have made their opinions known as well. We've listed some of them below. Do any of them match your definition? Indicate whether you strongly agree, agree, are not sure, disagree, or strongly disagree with each statement.

	Strongly Agree	Agree	Not Sure	Disagree	Strongly Disagree
Money, achievement, fame and success are important, but they are bought too dearly when acquired at the cost of health. — Anonymous					
It's great to be great, but it's better to be human. — Will Rogers					
Nothing succeeds like excess. — Oscar Wilde					
Success is a journey, not a destination. — Ben Sweetland					
The fastest way to succeed is to look as if you're playing by other people's rules, while quietly playing by your own. — Michael Korda					
She could not separate success from peace of mind. The two must go together . . . — Daphne Du Maurier, *Mary Anne*					
All of us are born for a reason, but all of us don't discover why. Success in life has nothing to do with what you gain in life or accomplish for yourself. It's what you do for others. — Danny Thomas					
I've never sought success in order to get fame and money; it's the talent and the passion that count in success. — Ingrid Bergman					
The two leading recipes for success are building a better mousetrap and finding a bigger loophole. — Edgar A. Shoaff					
Success is something to enjoy — to flaunt! Otherwise, why work so hard to get it? — Isobel Lennart, *Funny Girl*					
Success is knowing what your values are and living in a way consistent with your values. — Danny Cox					
Success can only be measured in terms of distance traveled… — Mavis Gallant					
If at first you don't succeed, you are running about average. — M. H. Anderson					
I think success has no rules, but you can learn a great deal from failure. — Jean Kerr, *Mary, Mary*					

	Strongly Agree	Agree	Not Sure	Disagree	Strongly Disagree
Success can make you go one of two ways. It can make you a *prima donna,* or it can smooth the edges, take away the insecurities, let the nice things come out. — Barbara Walters					
Six essential qualities that are the key to success: Sincerity, personal integrity, humility, courtesy, wisdom, charity. — Dr. William Menninger					
The people who try to do something and fail are infinitely better than those who try to do nothing and succeed. — Lloyd Jones					
The wealthy man is the man who is much, not the one who has much. — Karl Marx					
Winning isn't everything — it's the only thing. — Vince Lombardi					
Only those who dare to fail greatly can ever achieve greatly. — Robert F. Kennedy					
If at first you don't succeed, try, try again. Then give up. There's no use being a fool about it. — W. C. Fields					
I'm opposed to millionaires, but it would be dangerous to offer me the position. — Mark Twain					

Making Career Choices

Write your own definition of success here:

_____

_____

_____

_____

your name

Which decision-making patterns do you use most often? Explain.

_____

_____

_____

Chapter 2

Vocabulary List

aesthetics _____

forthright _____

forceful _____

authoritative _____

influencing _____

spontaneous _____

amiable _____

methodical _____

analytical _____

meticulous _____

diplomatic _____

systematic _____

submissive _____

charismatic _____

empathy _____

innovative _____

perseverance _____

versatile _____

synthesize _____

negotiate _____

Your Personal Profile

Write your name in the center of the chart, then add as many words as you can that describe your own passions, values, strengths, and so forth. As you fill out your chart, keep in mind that everyone has many different sides. Don't worry if some of your answers seem incompatible with others.

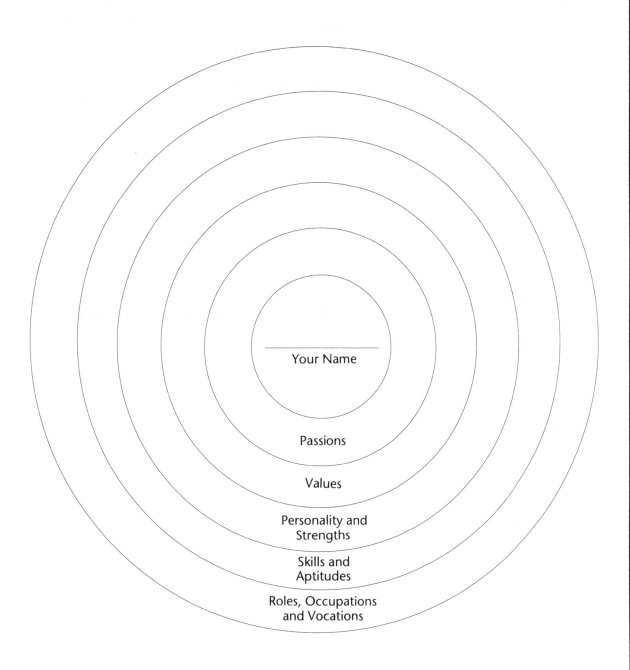

Your Name

Passions

Values

Personality and
Strengths

Skills and
Aptitudes

Roles, Occupations
and Vocations

Now assign a numerical value to each of your answers. Statements in the "very true" column are worth 9 points. Those you marked "sometimes true" get 6. Allow 3 points for each "not sure," and zero points for every "not true" answer.

In the columns below, write the numerical value of your response next to the statement number. For example, if you answered "very true" to the first statement, you would write a 9 on the line next to the number 1. When you have entered a number on each line, go back and total the columns under each heading.

ANSWERS

ADVENTURE	FAMILY	POWER	RECOGNITION	HELPING OTHERS
4. _____	8. _____	12. _____	11. _____	1. _____
16. _____	19. _____	29. _____	37. _____	26. _____
22. _____	27. _____	39. _____	48. _____	36. _____
38. _____	53. _____	47. _____	79. _____	43. _____
68. _____	65. _____	55. _____	86. _____	52. _____
76. _____	77. _____	60. _____	91. _____	85. _____
88. _____	81. _____	71. _____	101. _____	96. _____
92. _____	100. _____	90. _____	103. _____	99. _____
Total _____	Total _____	Total _____	Total _____	Total _____

PERSONAL INTEGRITY and MORAL COURAGE	FRIENDSHIP and COMPANION-SHIP	KNOWLEDGE and TRUTH	BEAUTY and AESTHETICS	INDEPENDENCE and FREEDOM
21. _____	2. _____	7. _____	14. _____	5. _____
33. _____	10. _____	13. _____	20. _____	25. _____
44. _____	35. _____	23. _____	30. _____	31. _____
58. _____	42. _____	46. _____	32. _____	51. _____
63. _____	56. _____	57. _____	54. _____	64. _____
83. _____	95. _____	61. _____	67. _____	70. _____
93. _____	102. _____	73. _____	69. _____	80. _____
97. _____	104. _____	87. _____	75. _____	94. _____
Total _____	Total _____	Total _____	Total _____	Total _____

CREATIVITY	MONEY	SECURITY
6. _____	18. _____	3. _____
9. _____	28. _____	15. _____
34. _____	41. _____	17. _____
59. _____	45. _____	24. _____
66. _____	50. _____	40. _____
84. _____	62. _____	49. _____
89. _____	74. _____	72. _____
98. _____	78. _____	82. _____
Total _____	Total _____	Total _____

In which category did you have the highest total? Right now, that value is most important to you. Remember, though, that values often change over time. You might want to come back to this survey every few years or when you are considering a change in your plans.

Did you have high scores in more than one category? If so, you might want to try to find a career that satisfies both or all your top values. If you value both beauty and adventure, for example, you might be happier tracking down international jewel thieves than you would be working in an art gallery or museum.

Strengths and Personality

In the four columns below, you will find a list of personality traits. Circle a total of 10 traits you feel best describe you.

a.	b.	c.	d.
forthright	enthusiastic	steady	analytical
adventurous	expressive	amiable	controlling
forceful	influencing	predictable	perfectionist
sharp	emotional	supportive	systematic
decisive	inventive	loyal	conventional
risk taker	spontaneous	methodical	respectful
demanding	trusting	team player	meticulous
authoritative	outgoing	calm	well-disciplined
direct	unselfish	thorough	diplomatic
curious	self-assured	dependable	precise
competitive	charming	self-composed	sensitive
self-sufficient	inspiring	possessive	accurate

Now total the number circled in each column:

_____

Complete the following self-evaluation quiz. Circle the letter under each situation that best reflects how you would be likely to act, feel, or think.

41

1. Your favorite projects are ones that are
   a. likely to have favorable results.
   b. enjoyable to take part in.
   c. clearly explained.
   d. detail oriented.

2. You are on the spring dance committee. You would be happiest
   a. chairing the committee.
   b. publicizing the event and selling tickets.
   c. decorating the hall.
   d. keeping track of the monies collected.

3. When doing your homework, you
   a. complete it in the shortest time possible.
   b. allow interruptions to take phone calls from friends.
   c. are willing to take time to help another student with the assignment.
   d. take time to check all your work for accuracy and thoroughness.

4. When faced with a stressful situation, you
   a. take charge and sometimes override the decisions of others.
   b. confront and may act in an impulsive fashion.
   c. become submissive and allow others to make your decisions.
   d. resist change and withdraw from the situation.

5. When getting dressed in the morning, you
   a. know exactly what you want to wear without giving it much thought.
   b. try on three things before deciding which is best.
   c. put on the clothes you laid out the night before.
   d. have no problem coordinating outfits because everything in your closet is in color sequence.

6. Your family is moving across the country to a lovely new home. You feel
   a. excited.
   b. curious.
   c. cautious.
   d. worried.

7. When you ask someone a question about a problem, you like an answer that
   a. is direct and to the point.
   b. includes stimulating ideas on various ways the problem could be solved.
   c. outlines the process for solving the problem.
   d. includes data and background on how the solution was reached.

8. When solving a problem, you are
   a. decisive.
   b. spontaneous.
   c. considered.
   d. deliberate.

9. When going shopping for clothes, you
   a. will not need a list. If you forget something, you'll just get it later.
   b. buy whatever catches your eye. You don't worry how different outfits go together.
   c. have a list and visit every store in town before finalizing your purchases.
   d. know exactly what you want and have studied the newspaper for sales.

18

1. How many of each letter did you choose?

a. _____

b. _____

c. _____

d. _____

Did you choose four or more of the same letter?   Yes   No

If so, which letter? _____

Now turn back to page 39.

How many characteristics did you circle in each column?

a. _____

b. _____

c. _____

d. _____

In which column did you place the most circles? _____

Does that letter match the predominant letter from the self-evaluation quiz on page 41?

If so, you can start identifying your work behavior style.

Permission granted to adapt from the Personal Profile System by Carlson Learning Company®.

Your Strengths

44

What are your strengths?

_____

_____

_____

_____

_____

_____

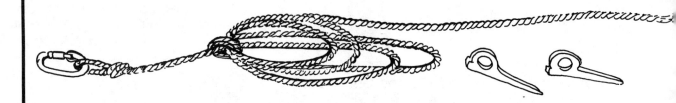

45

Now complete the chart below. Choose eight of the personal strengths you have identified and list them in the first column. Then, in the second column, describe a situation or personal experience where you used these strengths or where they might be helpful.

I AM:	I HAVE USED THIS STRENGTH TO:
1. _____	_____
2. _____	_____
3. _____	_____
4. _____	_____
5. _____	_____
6. _____	_____
7. _____	_____
8. _____	_____
9. _____	_____
10. _____	_____

Name That Skill

Use the following exercise to begin the list of skills you've mastered. Write three accomplishments that gave you the most satisfaction, or that you're most proud of, on the lines below. Then, in the middle column, list the skills you used in that enterprise. If you have a hard time identifying these skills, describe the experience to friends or family members and ask them to help you. (You'll complete the last column later.)

Accomplishment	Skills Required	Skills Catagory D, P, or T
1.		
2.		
3.		

Do you see any pattern in the kinds of skills you used? (Did they involve physical strength or coordination? Numbers or equations? Reasoning? Dealing with people?)

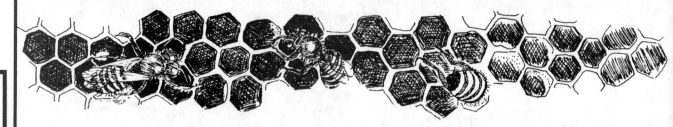

Skills Identification

Review your list of skills on the previous page. In the far right column place a D next to any skill used with data or information. Place a P next to those skills used with people and a T next to those used with material, equipment, or products. Do you seem to have a preference for any one skill category?

Use the chart below to list additional skills you currently have working with data, people, or things.

DATA	PEOPLE	THINGS

Can you think of skills you have not yet acquired that you would like to learn? List them below.

What messages have *you* received? For the following exercise, write what you think the significant people in your life would tell you about your future. Imagine them leaving their messages on your telephone answering machine.

Hello, you have reached _____'s message center. What would you like to tell me about my future?   BEEP!

Mother's message: _____

_____

Father's message: _____

_____

Teacher's message: _____

_____

Other significant adult's message (coach, mentor, boss, relative): _____

_____

_____

Best friend's message: _____

_____

Girlfriend or boyfriend's message: _____

_____

Society's message:

_____

_____

_____

Now go back and circle the messages that are limiting or negative. How much importance should you place on other people's opinions of you and their plans for your life? Should you have to live up to other people's goals and ideals? Whose life is it, anyway?

What positive messages can you give yourself about your future? Write them below. Recite them to yourself often. Or read them into a tape recorder and play them again and again while you're relaxing.

1. _____

_____

2. _____

_____

3. _____

_____

4. _____

_____

5. _____

_____

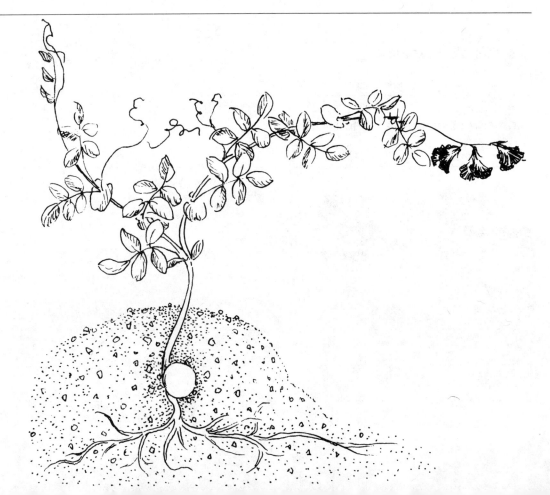

Chapter 3

Vocabulary List

self-actualization _____

_____

esteem _____

_____

survival _____

_____

capable _____

_____

necessity _____

_____

satisfaction _____

_____

hierarchy _____

_____

legacy _____

_____

acknowledge _____

_____

epitaph _____

_____

lifestyle _____

_____

sociology _____

_____

psychology _____

_____

component _____

_____

contemplation _____

_____

spiritual _____

_____

recuperate _____

_____

external _____

_____

internal _____

_____

priority _____

_____

Where Are You Now?

Answer the following questions to determine your present location on the Maslow Triangle. If you answer yes to the questions in each section, color in the corresponding section on the triangle below.

SURVIVAL

Do you have enough food and water to survive?	Yes	No
Do you have a place to live?	Yes	No
Do you have enough clothes to keep you warm?	Yes	No

SECURITY AND SAFETY

Do you feel safe?	Yes	No
Do you feel secure?	Yes	No

SENSE OF BELONGING

Do you feel you belong somewhere?	Yes	No
Do you feel loved?	Yes	No

SELF-ESTEEM

Do you feel good about yourself?	Yes	No
Do you feel worthwhile or valuable as a human being?	Yes	No

SELF-ACTUALIZATION

Do you feel accomplished?	Yes	No
Do you feel mature?	Yes	No
Do you trust your judgment?	Yes	No
Do you feel in control of your life?	Yes	No

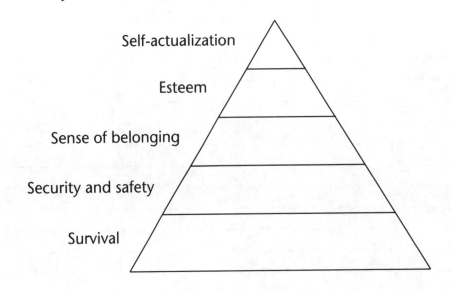

How Do You Want To Be Remembered?

In the space below, write your own epitaph. How do you want to be remembered? At the end of your life, what would you have to have done in order to be thought of that way? You don't have to limit your answer to a single line, but keep it brief.

_____ : _____

Your name

_____

_____

What About Your Life?

Shade the triangle below to show the balance in your life right now. Do you need to make any adjustments? What could you do to make your life more satisfying?

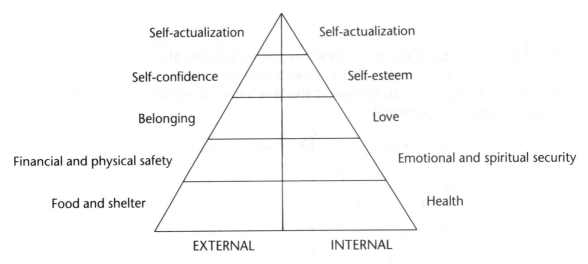

Now interview one of your parents or another adult you know and interpret his or her responses to the above questions. Shade the triangle below to show his or her balance.

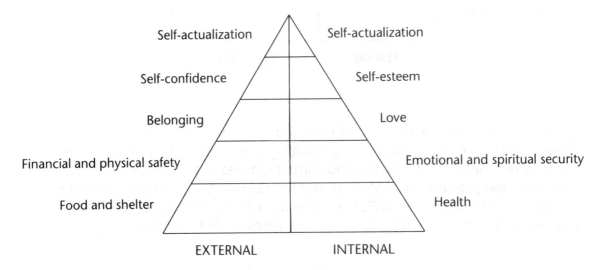

What do you think the triangle of a homeless person living alone would look like?

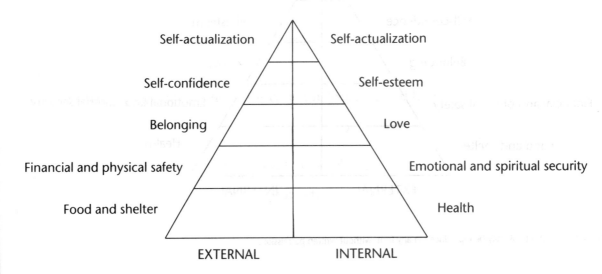

Chapter 4

Vocabulary List

privacy _____

commitment _____

profile _____

widow _____

aristocrat _____

affectability _____

variable _____

extensive _____

liberal _____

reallocate _____

poverty _____

conscious _____

traits _____

minimum _____

windfall _____

arrogant _____

persistence _____

dividends _____

inducement _____

interpretation _____

Your Budget

Let's talk about the kind of lifestyle you want to have — and how much money it is likely to cost. The following exercise asks you to make choices about everything from where you'd like to live to the vacations you'd like to take. Charts are provided to show approximately how much each choice costs (in today's dollars). Make your choice in each category, find the appropriate figure on the charts, and enter your monthly expense for each choice in the space provided.

Since the point of the exercise is to help you make career decisions for your future, don't base your choices on what you think is realistic for you right now. Instead, think of the way you would like to be living at some specific age in the future (make it at least 29 years old).

Choose an age and then complete this statement: Today I am _____ years old. In _____ years, when I am _____ years old, this is how I would like my life to look.

FAMILY PROFILE

The first choice you need to make concerns your future family. In the real world, this choice is not totally under your control. But dream away. Check the marital status you see for yourself at the age you've chosen, and the number of children you'll have, if any. Fill in the ages of your children.

MARITAL STATUS	CHILDREN	AGES OF CHILDREN
☐ Single	0 _____	_____
☐ Married	1 _____	_____
☐ Divorced	2 _____	_____
☐ Separated	3 _____	_____
☐ Widowed	4 _____	_____
☐ Other	5 _____	_____
	6 _____	_____

OTHER DEPENDENTS

WHERE I WOULD LIKE TO LIVE

_____

_____

_____

_____

WHY?

_____

_____

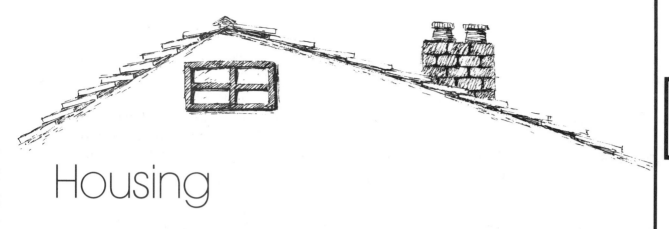

Housing

Housing is the most expensive item on most people's budget. It is possible that your future spouse, a titled aristocrat, will inherit the family estate (tax-free, of course). But don't count on it. For the purpose of this exercise, assume that you will have to allot a portion of your income for a place to live.

Keep your own values in mind as you complete this exercise. It's *your* dreams we're interested in, not your mom's or your best friend's.

Do you want to live in:

☐ Government housing   ☐ A farm or ranch

☐ A rental apartment   ☐ A cabin

☐ A cooperative apartment   ☐ A luxury home/estate

☐ A rental house   ☐ No permanent home

☐ Your own home   ☐ Other _____

☐ A condominium

How many bedrooms? _____ Bathrooms? _____

Other distinguishing features _____

_____

Check the classified advertisement section of a newspaper to get an idea of the sales price of homes and rental rates. The charts on the next page may help you figure your monthly costs.

Monthly payment/rent	$ _____
Monthly property taxes	$ _____
Monthly insurance	$ _____
Total utilities/phone	$ _____
Housing	$ _____ [1]

Enter at [1] on page 92, Your Budget Profile.
(Page 92 of *Career Choices* is located on
page 42 of this workbook.)

Transportation

Before you choose the kind of transportation you'll want or need, think about where you said you'd like to live. In some cities, it's quite easy to walk or use public transportation. In some places, a vehicle is almost a necessity. Consider, too, your physical condition and your mechanical ability.

Do you want to get around by:

☐ Walking

☐ Bicycle

☐ Motorcycle

☐ Public transportation

☐ Other

☐ Your own car, previously owned

☐ Your own car, bought new every 7-8 years

☐ Your own car, bought new every 3-4 years

☐ Your own car, bought new every year

If you want to own your own car:

What make _____   Model _____   Year _____

How many miles per month do you plan to drive? _____

Monthly car payments	$ _____
Gasoline	$ _____
Maintenance and insurance	$ _____
Public transportation	$ _____
Transportation	$ _____ [2]

Enter at [2] on page 92.

Clothing

Think about how much money you feel would be a reasonable amount to spend each year on clothing for yourself and each member of your family. How do you prefer to come by your clothes? Do you want or need an extensive wardrobe, or will just the basics do? Don't forget to make allotments for shoes, bathing suits, and other items that may not come immediately to mind. Then answer the questions below.

For clothing, I plan to:

☐ Sew for the family

☐ Purchase recycled clothing

☐ Buy from discount or economy catalogs and stores

☐ Always buy on sale

☐ Buy from department stores and boutiques

☐ Buy designer fashions

☐ Other _____

I would like to have:

☐ A minimum wardrobe

☐ A moderate-size wardrobe

☐ An extensive wardrobe

☐ What I want, when I want it

List each member of your family and his or her projected yearly clothing budget:

Family Member	Annual Budget
_____	$ _____
_____	$ _____
_____	$ _____
_____	$ _____
_____	$ _____
_____	$ _____
Annual family total	$ _____

Divide this figure by 12 to get your monthly clothing budget.

Clothing $ _____ [3]

Enter at [3] on page 92.

Food

Some years back a TV commercial featured a well-known naturalist who asked that memorable question, "Ever eat a pine tree?" He went on to inform viewers, "Some parts *are* edible." Perhaps. But most of us have come to expect more sophisticated fare. Still, there's plenty of room for negotiation between grazing in the forest and living solely on steak and caviar. The government has defined three kinds of food plans, each of which supplies the necessary nutrients. The Thrifty Plan is based on low-cost foods (beans, rice) but these may be unappealing to some people and may take more time for preparation. The Moderate Plan offers a greater variety of foods. The Liberal Plan lets you buy whatever you want regardless of the cost.

Would you like your diet to be based on:

☐ Government surplus food   ☐ The Moderate Plan

☐ The low-cost Thrifty Plan   ☐ The Liberal Plan

Do you have any special dietary habits that might increase your food budge (i.e., gourmet cooking is your hobby, you have a restricted diet)? The chart on page 85 may help you come up with an amount.

Food $ _____ [4]

Enter at [4] on page 92.

Sundries

Sundries are all those little things you pick up at the grocery or drug store: shampoo, deodorant, toilet paper, cleaning supplies, and the like. How much would you plan to spend on these items a month?

Sundries $ _____ [5]

Enter at [5] on page 92.

Entertainment and Recreation

Although the following budget items are not necessary to sustain life, they *do* have an impact on your self-esteem and life satisfaction. Answer the following questions, remembering to consider your spouse and your children's needs as well.

Monthly Total

How many times/month will you eat at a restaurant? _____

What will your average bill be? $ _____

How much per month will be spent on meals out? $ _____

Would you like to entertain friends?

What would you spend per month? $ _____

Would you like to attend concerts, movies, theaters, sports events, and the like?

What would you spend per month? $ _____

Will you buy books or tapes? Subscribe to newspapers and magazines?

How much a month would you like to spend? $ _____

Will you have hobbies or take part in sports that cost money?

What? _____

How much will you need a month? $ _____

If you have children, what kinds of recreational/educational opportunities do you want for them? (Check their ages again.)

What? _____

How much will be spent per month? $ _____

One more consideration: Do you want to have special equipment related to entertainment or recreation? Would you like to have a stereo or CD player, VCR, musical instruments, computer, boat, plane, country club or health club membership?

What do you want to spend on them per month? $ _____

Total entertainment $ _____ [6]

Enter at [6] on page 92.

Vacations

This is not so much a "whether or not" budget item as it is a "where and how often" expenditure. It's been shown that taking time off is an important part of maintaining good physical and mental health. How do you want to do it?

Do you want to take a vacation:

☐ Monthly

☐ Every six months

☐ Yearly

☐ Every two years

☐ Every three to five years

☐ Other _____

What kind of vacation would you like to be able to afford:

☐ Car trip to relatives

☐ Camping/hiking

☐ Day trips to local amusements

☐ A week at the seashore or mountain cabin

☐ Car trips to places of interest

☐ Plane trips to places of interest

☐ Foreign travel

☐ Cruises, travel packages, or exotic clubs

☐ Other _____

☐ Other _____

What will you want to budget every year to meet your vacation objectives? $ _____

Divide that figure by 12 to come up with your monthly figure.

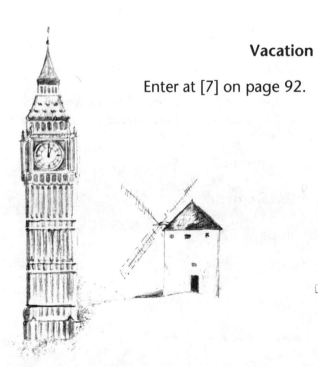

Vacation $ _____ [7]

Enter at [7] on page 92.

Child Care

If both parents are working while there are young children in the family (a reasonable assumption), you will need to consider your child care options. First, look back to see how many children you are planning to have and their ages.

Would you have:

☐ No need for child care

☐ A relative to care for them

☐ A cooperative arrangement with a relative or friend

☐ Care in a community-based center

☐ A private nursery school or day care center

☐ A sitter coming into your home

☐ Live-in help

How much will this cost per child, per month?

child one $ _____

child two $ _____

child three $ _____

Total child care costs $ _____ [8]

Enter at [8] on page 92.

DEPENDENT CARE

If you indicated at the beginning of this exercise that you plan to care for a dependent other than your children (a parent or grandparent, for example), remember to add that into your monthly budget. What do you plan to spend on dependent care? $ _____

What if there is a divorce or separation in your future? Will you need to pay alimony or child support? How much? $ _____ Keep these costs in mind as you plan for monthly reserves.

Health Care

Because an unforeseen accident or illness can play havoc with the most carefully planned budget, health insurance is a must. Many employers will subsidize your health insurance, but you usually will have to pay a portion of the cost. What kind of care do you want?

☐ Government-subsidized free clinics ☐ Private physician and dentist

☐ Health maintenance organization care

See page 94 for some sample annual costs. Divide your projected annual cost by 12 months.

Health care $ _____ [9]

Enter at [9] on page 92.

Furnishings

You probably need to purchase replacement equipment and items for your home such as linens, appliances, furniture and decorative items. Assume you have most of these items by this time.

Annual budget $ _____ divided by 12

Furnishings $ _____ [10]

Enter at [10] on page 92.

Savings

This is an important part of any budget. There are predictable things to save for (a house, new furnishings, children's college, retirement) as well as things you'd rather not think about (losing your job, a major illness). Spending money on a new roof or water heater isn't fun, but sometimes it has to be done. And it's a lot easier if you've planned for it. As a rule of thumb, every family should save at least six months' income in case of emergency.

What do you feel you should save each month for:

☐ Emergencies ☐ Retirement

☐ Repairs, replacements, or major purchases ☐ Income cushion

☐ Children's college

Savings $ _____ [11]

Enter at [11] on page 92.

Miscellaneous

Are there things important to you that we haven't mentioned yet? Think about your values. Here are some possible additional expenses. Add your own if you need to.

What will be your monthly budget for holiday gifts and birthdays?

$ _____

Will you have pets? If so, what kind? _____

How much per month will it cost to keep them?

$ _____

Will you make contributions to social, political, or religious organizations?
If so, how much per month?

$ _____

Do you want to send your children to private schools?   Yes   No   Undecided

How much will this cost per month? $ _____

Other costs, list:

_____ $ _____

_____ $ _____

_____ $ _____

Miscellaneous $ _____ [12]

Enter at [12] on page 92.

Your Budget Profile

Here's the moment of truth. Go through the exercise again and enter the monthly amounts you indicated in each category in the appropriate space below. Then add the column to come up with your total monthly budget.

[1] Housing $ _____

[2] Transportation $ _____

[3] Clothing $ _____

[4] Food $ _____

[5] Sundries $ _____

[6] Entertainment $ _____

[7] Vacations $ _____

[8] Child care $ _____

[9] Health care $ _____

[10] Furnishings $ _____

[11] Savings $ _____

[12] Miscellaneous $ _____

Total: $ _____

What Salary Will Support this Lifestyle?

To find the monthly salary you will need to cover your expenses, divide your monthly expenses by 80 percent.

Expenses (or net pay) divided by 80% = Gross pay

_____ ÷ 80% = _____
total from page 92   your required monthly salary

Multiply this figure by 12 (months) to get the annual salary figure required.

_____ X 12 = _____
your required monthly salary   your required annual salary

Back to your budget. Did the figure you arrived at on page 92 seem higher than the salary you're likely to earn on your own? What amount do you think you could reasonably expect to earn? Write that figure on line b below. Next determine your net income (line a), if you earn that salary (see formula page 93). Now reallocate your funds. Write the adjusted figures for your hard times budget below. The total should be a figure no larger than your *own* income. Don't count on your phantom spouse here.

HARD TIMES BUDGET

1. Housing	$	_____
2. Transportation	$	_____
3. Clothing	$	_____
4. Food	$	_____
5. Sundries	$	_____
6. Entertainment	$	_____
7. Vacations	$	_____
8. Child care	$	_____
9. Health care	$	_____
10. Furnishings	$	_____
11. Savings	$	_____
12. Miscellaneous	$	_____
a) Total:	$	_____
b) Gross monthly salary	$	_____

WILL'S BUDGET

1. Housing $ _____   8. Child care $ _____

2. Transportation $ _____   9. Health care $ _____

3. Clothing $ _____   10. Furnishings $ _____

4. Food $ _____   11. Savings $ _____

5. Sundries $ _____   12. Miscellaneous $ _____

6. Entertainment $ _____   **Total:** $ _____$550_____

7. Vacations $ _____

What is the gross monthly income required to come up

with this net? $ _____

JEFF AND FRANCIE'S BUDGET

1. Housing $ _____   8. Child care $ _____

2. Transportation $ _____   9. Health care $ _____

3. Clothing $ _____   10. Furnishings $ _____

4. Food $ _____   11. Savings $ _____

5. Sundries $ _____   12. Miscellaneous $ _____

6. Entertainment $ _____   **Total:** $ _____$2,300_____

7. Vacations $ _____

Total: $1,500/month take-home salary, Jeff
                $800/month take-home salary, Francie

What is the gross monthly income required to come up with this net? $ _____

RUTH AND CARL'S BUDGET

1. Housing $ _____
2. Transportation $ _____
3. Clothing $ _____
4. Food $ _____
5. Sundries $ _____
6. Entertainment $ _____
7. Vacations $ _____

8. Child care $ _____
9. Health care $ _____
10. Furnishings $ _____
11. Savings $ _____
12. Miscellaneous $ _____
    Total: $ ___$5,000___

    Total: $2,800/month take-home salary, Carl
            $3,200/month take-home salary, Ruth

What is the gross monthly income required to come up with this net? $ _____

BEN AND LYNN'S BUDGET

1. Housing $ _____
2. Transportation $ _____
3. Clothing $ _____
4. Food $ _____
5. Sundries $ _____
6. Entertainment $ _____
7. Vacations $ _____

8. Child care $ _____
9. Health care $ _____
10. Furnishings $ _____
11. Savings $ _____
12. Miscellaneous $ _____
    Total: $ ___$2,300___

    Total: $2300/month take-home salary

What is the gross monthly income required to come up with this net? $ _____

Could You Become a Poverty Statistic?

103

What do you think contributes to poverty in this country?

_____

_____

_____

What might cause you to become one of these statistics?

_____

_____

How can you prevent that from happening?

_____

_____

_____

LEON'S STORY

107

What are the sacrifices Leon has made?

_____

Which values do these sacrifices reflect?

_____

What are Leon's rewards?

_____

Which values do they reflect?

_____

Do you share Leon's values?   Yes   No   Undecided

Are you willing to make similar sacrifices?   Yes   No   Undecided

VINCENT'S STORY

What are the sacrifices Vincent has made?

_____

Which values do they reflect?

_____

What are Vincent's rewards?

_____

Which values do they reflect?

_____

Do you share Vincent's values?   Yes   No   Undecided

Would you be ready to make similar sacrifices?   Yes   No   Undecided

SARA'S STORY

What sacrifices has Sara had to make? _____

_____

_____

What values categories would you put them under?

_____

_____

List Sara's rewards. _____

_____

_____

To which values categories do they belong? _____

_____

Do you and Sara have similar values?   Yes   No   Undecided

Would you be willing to make the same sacrifices?   Yes   No   Undecided

  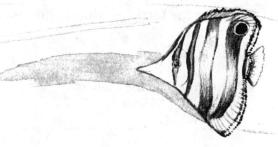

ROSE'S STORY

What sacrifices has Rose made for her career? _____

_____

What values categories would you place them in? _____

_____

What are her rewards? _____

_____

What values do you think they mirror? _____

_____

Are your values similar to Rose's?   Yes   No   Undecided

Would you make the same sacrifices?   Yes   No   Undecided

You Win Some, You Lose Some

Every job has its rewards and its sacrifices. How well a given career could work for you depends on your own values. It's important to recognize which values are compatible with a job and which are not. See how adept you are at recognizing which traits a job will call forth, and which it will deny. For each of the following careers, list the values you think will be rewarded and those that will most likely be sacrificed.

Soldier
Rewards: Adventure
Sacrifices: Freedom, creativity

Computer programmer
Rewards: Security, creativity
Sacrifices: Beauty and aesthetics, adventure

Professional athlete
Rewards: Recognition, power, adventure
Sacrifices: Freedom, security

Fire fighter
Rewards: _____

Sacrifices: _____

Veterinarian
Rewards: _____

Sacrifices: _____

Fashion model
Rewards: _____

Sacrifices: _____

Radio Announcer
Rewards: _____

Sacrifices: _____

Social worker
Rewards: _____

Sacrifices: _____

Mechanic
Rewards: _____

Sacrifices: _____

Farmer
Rewards: _____

Sacrifices: _____

Truck driver
Rewards: _____

Sacrifices: _____

Flight attendant
Rewards: _____

Sacrifices: _____

Homemaker
Rewards: _____

Sacrifices: _____

Garbage hauler
Rewards: _____

Sacrifices: _____

Accountant
Rewards: _____

Sacrifices: _____

Resort owner
Rewards: _____

Sacrifices: _____

On each of the following lines, you'll find an occupation followed by a list of values. Circle those values you think would be met by the career. Then, on the line provided, state what this person might do to meet the other need.

Social worker: helping others   creativity   power _____

Assembly line worker: helping others   security   friendship _____

Carpenter: adventure   beauty and aesthetics   family _____

Sales representative: family   money   friendship _____

Homemaker: family   helping others   power _____

Museum guide: beauty and aesthetics   adventure   creativity _____

Professor: knowledge   creativity   recognition _____

Farmer: family   helping others   friendship _____

Psychologist: adventure   helping others   beauty and aesthetics _____

Accountant: power   money   creativity _____

Chemist: knowledge   creativity   recognition _____

Writer: creativity   helping others   friendship _____

Veterinarian: helping others   knowledge   power _____

An Investment in Education . . .

. . . Yields Dividends for a Lifetime

The chart below shows more dramatically how each year of education affects future earnings.

How many years do you plan to work between the age of 18 and 65?

_____ years in workforce

Multiply the number of years you plan to be in the workforce with each of the annual salaries listed below to find out how much you would earn over the course of your working life.

$10,000 x _____ years in workforce = $ _____ lifetime earnings

$15,000 x _____ years in workforce = $ _____ lifetime earnings

$20,000 x _____ years in workforce = $ _____ lifetime earnings

$30,000 x _____ years in workforce = $ _____ lifetime earnings

$50,000 x _____ years in workforce = $ _____ lifetime earnings

What is the difference between a $10,000 and $15,000 annual salary

over a lifetime? $ _____

What is the difference between a $10,000 and $20,000 annual salary

over a lifetime? $ _____

What is the difference between a $10,000 and $30,000 annual salary

over a lifetime? $ _____

What is the difference between a $10,000 and $50,000 annual salary

over a lifetime? $ _____

75

70

65

60

55

50

45

40

35

30

25

20

15

10

5

High School

Junior High School

Elementary School

Maybe the time required to get the education and training for a job that interests you still seems too long, higher income or no. Let's look at it another way.

The bar graph below represents an average lifespan — about 78 years. We've already filled it in for a high school graduate. That leaves you about 60 years to play around with. How will you spend that time?

Think about the kind of life you'd like to have, the job that appeals to you most, no matter how long the training required. Using the following questions as a guide, fill in the graph.

Using *polka dots* fill in and label the block of time for *post-high school training*.

Using *horizontal stripes* fill in and label the block(s) of time for *working full-time* and diagonal lines for *working part-time*.

Using *stars* fill in and label the block(s) of *time* for *outside the workforce* for raising a family or retirement.

Use the information from your graph to answer the following questions.

How many years of post-high school training will you complete?

_____ years = a

How many years do you think you will work outside the home full-time?

_____ years = b

How many years do you think you will work outside the home part-time?

_____ years = c

Here are some interesting facts about your worklife.

How many hours might you work in your lifetime?

full-time   2,080 hours/year x _____ (b) = _____ f

part-time   1,000 hours/year x _____ (c) = _____ g

f _____ + g _____ = _____ hours you will work

in your lifetime.

That's a lot of time to be doing something that you do not find satisfying . . . that doesn't correspond to your values or passions . . . that doesn't meet your lifestyle desires.

O.K. let's look at it one more way . . .

For every year of post-high school education, you will work _____ years.

Hint: $\dfrac{b + c}{a}$ = _____ h

Next time you think, "Yuck, I can't stay in school _____ more years! I didn't want to be a _____ anyway!" Remember these figures. Education and training now are a small investment when you look at the long-range payoffs in life satisfaction. Hang in there . . . you'll be glad you did!

Ask Someone Who's Been There

The information in this book is necessarily more general than we would like. To get some specific answers to the questions *you* have, interview three people over the age of 29. Use the following questions to help determine the rewards and sacrifices each person's job brings with it.

NAME _____

OCCUPATION _____

HOW LONG IN THIS OCCUPATION ? _____

How did you choose your occupation? _____

_____

Financially, does it let you live the way you prefer? _____

_____

If not, why not and what can you do about it? _____

_____

What rewards have you experienced? _____

          (Listen carefully here. Keep the different values categories in mind.)

    Values interpretation: _____

What sacrifices have you had to make for your career? _____

    Values interpretation: _____

What kind of commitment does this career require in terms of:

    Education _____

    Energy/endurance _____

    Stick-to-itiveness _____

If you had it to do over again, would you choose this career? _____

Why or why not? _____

Easier Said Than Done

Kay wants to save money for college. Her friend wants Kay to go with her on a ski vacation.

Jamal wants to do well at his weekend job. He feels like sleeping in on Saturday morning.

Lee wants to be in the school play. The thought of auditioning for a part makes him anxious.

Juanita wants to study art in France. Because of a scheduling problem, taking a French class would mean giving up her place in the school choir.

Complete this chart for Kay, Jamal, Lee and Juanita.
What do you want? Look back to the goals you set in chapter 3 and fill in the chart.
Use this model to help make day-to-day decisions about realizing your dreams.

	It's easier to . . .	. . . than	But what I want is . . .	. . . therefore I will . . . .
Kay Jamal Lee Juanita You				

Chapter 5

Vocabulary List

category _____

_____

characteristics _____

_____

environment _____

_____

frequent _____

_____

acquaintances _____

_____

isolation _____

_____

variety _____

_____

compatible _____

_____

flexible _____

_____

potential _____

_____

incentive _____

_____

option _____

_____

composite _____

_____

free-lance _____

_____

sequential _____

_____

anxiety _____

_____

tolerance _____

_____

entrepreneur _____

_____

capital _____

_____

status _____

_____

On each of the following pages, you will find a brief description of a particular category of career considerations. A list of options involving that category follows. Check the box in front of any statement that appeals to you. Choose as many options as you like, but make sure they don't contradict each other. Feel free to add to the lists if we've overlooked something that appeals to you.

Physical Settings

Check the statements below that appeal to you.

- ☐ I would like to work in a city.
- ☐ I would like to work in the country.
- ☐ I would like to work in a small to medium-sized town.
- ☐ I would like to work in _____ (list a specific city or part of the country).
- ☐ I would like to work in another country _____
- ☐ I would like a job that might offer frequent transfers.
- ☐ I would like a job that will let me stay in one place.
- ☐ I would like a job that keeps me "on the road," traveling from place to place.
- ☐ I would like to work outdoors (list specifics if you can, i.e., in the woods, on a farm, at sea) _____
- ☐ I would like to work out of a car or truck most of the time.
- ☐ I would like to work in an office.
- ☐ I would like to work in my home.
- ☐ It's important to me that my work setting be pleasing to the eye.
- ☐ I would like to work in a garage or warehouse.
- ☐ I would like to work in a factory.
- ☐ I would like a job that involves both indoor and outdoor work.
- ☐ I would like to work in a science lab or hospital.
- ☐ I would like to work in a retail store.
- ☐ I would like to work in a restaurant.
- ☐ I would like to work on a constuction site.
- ☐ I would like to work on a ship, plane, train, or bus.
- ☐ I would like to work in a hotel or resort.
- ☐ I would like to work in a museum or art gallery.
- ☐ I would like to work in an art or photography studio.
- ☐ I would like to work in a concert hall or theater.
- ☐ I would like to work in a school or library.
- ☐ I would like to work in a church or synagogue.
- ☐ I would like to work on the set of a movie or TV show.
- ☐ I would like to work in a TV, radio or recording studio.
- ☐ I would like to work in _____

Working Conditions

Check the statements below that appeal to you.

☐ I would like a job that requires me to "dress for success" (dress up for a professional office).

☐ I would like a job that requires me to wear a uniform or costume.

☐ I would like a job that lets me dress any way I want.

☐ I would like a job that lets me work alone most of the time.

☐ I would like a job that lets me work with the same group of people.

☐ I would like a job that lets me work with many different clients.

☐ I would like a job that lets me work with ideas.

☐ I would like a job that lets me work with information.

☐ I would like a job that lets me work with numbers.

☐ I would like a job that lets me work with machines.

☐ I would like a job that lets me work with tools.

☐ I would like a job that lets me be creative.

☐ I would like a job that involves physical labor or activity.

☐ I would like a job with prescribed duties and procedures.

☐ I would like a job with strict deadlines.

☐ I would like a job with structured working hours.

☐ I would like a job with somewhat flexible hours.

☐ I would like a job that lets me structure my time any way I want.

☐ I would like a job that often calls for putting in extra hours.

☐ I wouldn't mind working nights or weekends.

☐ I would like a job that involves risk or danger.

☐ I would like a job that might take away my privacy.

☐ I would like a job that is intellectually challenging.

☐ I would like a job I could forget about when I'm not there.

☐ I would like to be able to work part-time when my children are young.

☐ I would like a job that involves a variety of tasks and duties.

☐ Other _____

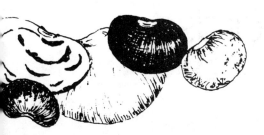

Relationships at Work

Check the statements below that appeal to you.

- ☐ I would like to work alone.
- ☐ I would like to work in a group or on a team.
- ☐ I would like to work with a variety of people.
- ☐ I would like to be the boss.
- ☐ I would like to be supervised by others.
- ☐ I would like to work for myself.
- ☐ I would like to work with adults.
- ☐ I would like to work with children.
- ☐ I would like to work with sick people.
- ☐ I would like to work with handicapped people.
- ☐ I would like to work with older people.
- ☐ I would like to work with creative people.
- ☐ I would like to work with people like me.
- ☐ I would like to work with people different from me.
- ☐ I would like to work with people who speak a different language.
- ☐ I would like to work with the underprivileged.
- ☐ I would like to teach people.
- ☐ I would like to entertain people.
- ☐ I would like to make people feel better.
- ☐ I would like to make people look better.
- ☐ I would like to help people get out of trouble.
- ☐ I would like to sell things to people.
- ☐ I would like to work with criminals.
- ☐ I would like to give people guidance.
- ☐ I would like to run for election to office.
- ☐ I would expect to socialize with my co-workers.
- ☐ I would like to meet celebrities on my job.
- ☐ I would like to work in a competitive environment.
- ☐ I would like a job where everyone works together for the common good.
- ☐ I would like to serve the public.
- ☐ I would like to serve private clients.
- ☐ Other _____

Psychological Rewards of Working

Check the statements below that appeal to you.

- ☐ I would like to be recognized in the community for the work I do.
- ☐ I would like a job where I am free to make my own decisions.
- ☐ I would like a job that furthers my mission in life.
- ☐ I would like a job that helps less fortunate members of the community.
- ☐ I would like a job that offer thrills and adventure.
- ☐ I would like a job that lets me put my family duties first.
- ☐ I would like a job in which I am continually learning something new.
- ☐ I would like a job that has high status in the community.
- ☐ I want to work with people I admire and respect.
- ☐ I would like a job that demands creativity and innovation.
- ☐ I would like to work for something I believe in, even if it is unpopular or puts me in danger.
- ☐ I would like a job that adds to the beauty in the world.
- ☐ I would like a job that adds to the safety of the world.
- ☐ I would like a position of power.
- ☐ I would like a job that gives me a lot of freedom.
- ☐ I want to feel secure that my job will be there as long as I want it.
- ☐ I would like to be applauded for my work.
- ☐ Other _____

Mixing Career and Family

Check the statements below that appeal to you.

- ☐ I want to be married.
- ☐ I want to have children.
- ☐ Family life is more important to me than my career.
- ☐ My career is more important to me than having a family.
- ☐ I would like both a rewarding career and a happy family life.
- ☐ I would like to stay home with my children when they are young.
- ☐ I would like my spouse to stay home with the children when they are young.
- ☐ I would like to work out of my house when my children are young.
- ☐ I would like a job with flexible hours so I can be available for my family.
- ☐ I would like to be able to afford to send my children to a day care pre-school.
- ☐ I would like to be able to afford to have a sitter come to the house.
- ☐ I would like to be able to afford to have live-in help with the children.
- ☐ I would like to be able to afford to have a housekeeper so I can spend more time with my family.
- ☐ I would expect my family to help out with household chores.
- ☐ Other _____

Financial Rewards

Check the statements below that appeal to you.

☐ I would like a job that pays at least $_____ per month. See page 91.

☐ I would like to be paid by the hour, with time and a half for overtime.

☐ I would like a monthly salary that doesn't vary with the number of hours I work.

☐ I would like to work on a commission basis.

☐ I would like a job that would be secure even in times of recession.

☐ I'm willing to accept a lower salary if the potential for either financial or psychological rewards is good.

☐ Money isn't important to me — I just need enough to get by.

☐ I want a job with good benefits (e.g., health insurance, pension plan, paid vacations).

☐ I'd like my salary to be based on my job performance.

☐ I'd like a job with scheduled pay increases.

☐ I'd like to be paid for the things I create or produce (e.g., paintings, articles, cookies).

☐ I'd like a job that offers bonuses or other incentives.

☐ I'm willing to start with a very low salary as long as there is an opportunity to work toward a very high salary.

☐ Other _____

Job Skills

This final category should help you fill out your general career outline. Check back to chapter two and record your findings below.

My physical skills include _____

_____

My intellectual and creative skills include _____

_____

My social skills include _____

_____

The skills I would like to acquire are (you will need to expand this list when you come up with a specific career goal)

_____

_____

134

You probably checked a number of statements in each category. Read them all again to get a *very* broad picture of your career desires. Since it's unlikely that any job could meet all these requirements, go back and choose the one or two statements from each category that mean the most to you. Circle the boxes in front of those statements. Then enter them on the following chart. Keep these in mind as you begin shortening your list of possible careers.

Your Chart

The physical setting I want to work in is: _____

The working conditions I would most enjoy include: _____

_____

I would like my work relationships to be: _____

_____

The psychological reward most important to me is: _____

_____

My goals for mixing career and family include: _____

_____

Financially, I would like: _____

_____

The skills I have or would most like to acquire include: _____

_____

Do your answers support any of the career choices you had in mind? Do they rule out any of them? Or do they suggest new possibilities?

Consider Your Options

On the chart below, circle the job characteristic on each line that appeals most to you.

Column 1	Column 2
Full-time	Part-time
Structured hours	Flexible hours
Employee	Employer
Salaried	Free-lance, commission
Single career	Composite careers
Lifetime career	Sequential careers

Did you circle more characteristics in column 1 or in column 2? _____

Column 1 represents careers with fewer risks, higher security, and less freedom. These careers also allow for a lower level of anxiety tolerance.

Column 2 represents careers with more risks, lower security, and more freedom. Careers like these usually call for a fairly high anxiety tolerance.

Do your choices feel right for you?	**Yes**	**No**	**Undecided**
Do you consider yourself a risk taker?	**Yes**	**No**	**Undecided**
Do you often worry about future events or situations?	**Yes**	**No**	**Undecided**

Refer to this chart as you make your career decisions and explore different job titles. Would you be more comfortable in a job offering security or one providing more freedom? Although these characteristics are at opposite ends of the scale, one is not better than the other. It's entirely a matter of what feels right for you.

Employee or Employer?

ENTREPRENEURIAL CHECKLIST

Select the answer that best describes, or comes closest to, your feelings.

- ☐ 1. As long as I feel that there is a good chance of success, I'll go for it without hesitation.
- ☐ 2. I'm willing to invest some capital, but I always want to leave a sizable cushion, just in case.
- ☐ 3. I have never really felt comfortable risking money or time on things I'm not absolutely sure of.

Independence:

- ☐ 1. Most of all, I want to be my own boss; it's my major goal.
- ☐ 2. I don't mind working for other people, but I'd rather be on my own.
- ☐ 3. Being on my own really scares me. I'd rather have the security of being an employee, and let someone else worry about the problems.

Flexibility:

- ☐ 1. I adapt to change quickly and decisively.
- ☐ 2. I move, but it takes time and careful consideration.
- ☐ 3. I would rather see things stay the same; I get uptight when change occurs.

Self-confidence:

- ☐ 1. I am very confident in myself and know that I can handle most situations.
- ☐ 2. I am confident most of the time, particularly when I know the ground rules.
- ☐ 3. I'm not in control of my destiny; other people really control my future.

Attitude toward people:

- ☐ 1. I am naturally drawn to people; I like them, and they like me.
- ☐ 2. I find most people enjoyable, and most people are attracted to me.
- ☐ 3. I like things more than people and don't have many friends.

Knowledge of the particular business:

- ☐ 1. I know the business that I've been thinking about well and will enjoy it.
- ☐ 2. I'm reasonably confident I can learn the business, and it appears that I will enjoy it.
- ☐ 3. I am not familiar with this type of business, nor do I know whether I will enjoy it.

Ability to start from scratch:

- ☐ 1. I enjoy the challenge of building something from scratch on my own; I'm a self-starter.
- ☐ 2. If given basic guidelines, I can do a good job.
- ☐ 3. I really prefer to have the entire job laid out, then I'll do it well.

Commitment:

- ☐ 1. I have a high drive and commitment, and won't stop until the project is done.
- ☐ 2. I seem to have a higher level of perseverance when things are going well.
- ☐ 3. I start many projects, but rarely find time to finish them.

Common sense:

☐ 1. I consider myself realistic and "street wise" when it comes to business.

☐ 2. Most business situations make sense, but there are areas where I feel out of step.

☐ 3. I am inexperienced and impractical in business matters.

Willingness to accept failure:

☐ 1. "Nothing ventured, nothing gained" is my motto.

☐ 2. I want to succeed, but if I fail, I will accept it.

☐ 3. I want to avoid failure, and won't take a risk if it doesn't look like a sure thing.

Health:

☐ 1. I have excellent health and feel good, both physically and mentally.

☐ 2. I get sick on occasion, but it doesn't last long.

☐ 3. I have problems with my health, illness always seems to get in my way.

Work habits:

☐ 1. I plan before I start and then work my plan; I'm well-organized.

☐ 2. I find that I'm organized most of the time; but on occasion, I do get out of control.

☐ 3. I take things as they come, and sometimes get priorities confused.

To total your score, add up all the checked numbers. A number one has the weight of one, a number two scores a two and a three equals three. If your total score is between 12 and 16, you are a good candidate and should consider starting your own business at some time.

Reprinted with permission: *How To Start, Expand and Sell A Business, A Complete Guidebook for Entrepreneurs* by James C. Comiskey.

What About Status?

What does status mean to you? Whose opinions matter to you most? What values does status reflect? Can you explain why, today, a rock star has more status than a teacher or a politician? Consider these questions and then, to help clarify your thoughts, indicate whether you agree or disagree with the following statements.

It is important to me to have a job with high status.

Agree   Disagree

I am willing to invest the time it takes to train for a job with high status.

Agree   Disagree

It is more important to me that a job has status than that it pays well.

Agree   Disagree

I don't think I could be happy at a job that others might look down on.

Agree   Disagree

Chapter 6

Vocabulary List

artistic _____

accommodate _____

protective _____

humanitarian _____

occupation _____

tentative _____

excursion _____

attributes _____

visualization _____

typical _____

mesh _____

consult _____

accurate _____

explicit _____

decisive _____

gregarious _____

contagious _____

patient _____

conscientious _____

prominent _____

Bring In Your Identity

The career interest areas are set up so that the jobs listed in each category reflect similar values. Turn back to your Bull's Eye Chart on page 27 to review your values and passions (passions also reflect your values). Now go over the interest areas again. Below, list one or two that appeal to you most, or that seem to complement your values and passions.

_____

_____

While you're at it, take another look at your strengths and skills. Do you see (or can you think of) any careers within your chosen interest area(s) that also seem to fit in with these aspects of your personality? List some possible careers on the following lines. (Don't forget to consult your chart from chapter 5!)

_____

_____

_____

Career Interest Survey

Now it's time to choose three careers that appeal to you most and begin learning as much about them as you can. Review the careers chosen on page 147. It will be helpful if you can interview people now working in these fields as well. Separate worksheets are provided for each job.

JOB TITLE _____

1. What specific tasks would I perform on this job? (For example, a salesclerk would answer questions, tidy displays, unpack merchandise, write sales slips, make change, and so on.)

_____

_____

2. What is the job environment likely to be? Is this compatible with the setting I said I wanted on *page 126*?

_____

_____

3. What would be the rewards of working at this job? Are they the same as the ones I listed on *page 129*?

_____

_____

4. I would find this job particularly satisfying because: (Review your passions, values, interests, and life goals for guidance.) *See page 27.*

_____

_____

5. Is this job compatible with my work behavioral style? If so, in what ways? (Don't feel obliged to answer this question unless you have been able to take the complete Personal Profile System.)

_____

_____

6. How much training or education would I need? Where could I get it? Am I willing to make this kind of commitment? *Review pages 116 – 120.*

_____

_____

7. Does this job require specific physical attributes or abilities (strength or health requirements, 20/20 vision, and so on)? If so, what are they? Do I meet them?

_____

_____

8. What could I expect to earn as a beginner in this field? _____

What is the average mid-career salary? _____

9. Does this meet my salary requirements? *See pages 91 and 131.*   Yes   No

_____

10. What is the projected outlook for this career? Will there be many job openings when I am ready to go to work?

_____

_____

11. What aptitudes, strengths, and talents does this job call for? Do I have them? Can I get them? *See page 132.*

_____

_____

12. What can I do today to begin preparing for this job?

_____

_____

13. What classes must I take in high school to qualify for this job?

_____

_____

14. Where in this town or state could I find a job in this field?

_____

15. How does this career mesh with my family plans? Is it consistent with my desired lifestyle? *See page 130.* Does it offer opportunities for flexible hours or part-time work? Is the income high enough so I could maintain my family on it alone if necessary? Could I afford the kind of day care I'd like for my children?

_____

_____

_____

16. Are there opportunities for self-employment in this field (free-lance work, consulting, and the like)?

_____

_____

JOB TITLE _____

1. What specific tasks would I perform on this job? (For example, a salesclerk would answer questions, tidy displays, unpack merchandise, write sales slips, make change, and so on.)

_____

_____

2. What is the job environment likely to be? Is this compatible with the setting I said I wanted on *page 126*?

_____

_____

3. What would be the rewards of working at this job? Are they the same as the ones I listed on *page 129*?

_____

_____

4. I would find this job particularly satisfying because: (Review your passions, values, interests, and life goals for guidance.) *See page 27.*

_____

_____

5. Is this job compatible with my work behavioral style? If so, in what ways? (Don't feel obliged to answer this question unless you have been able to take the complete Personal Profile System.)

_____

_____

6. How much training or education would I need? Where could I get it? Am I willing to make this kind of commitment? *Review pages 116 – 120.*

_____

_____

7. Does this job require specific physical attributes or abilities (strength or health requirements, 20/20 vision, and so on)? If so, what are they? Do I meet them?

_____

_____

8. What could I expect to earn as a beginner in this field? _____

What is the average mid-career salary? _____

9. Does this meet my salary requirements? *See pages 91 and 131.*   Yes   No

_____

10. What is the projected outlook for this career? Will there be many job openings when I am ready to go to work?

_____

_____

11. What aptitudes, strengths, and talents does this job call for? Do I have them? Can I get them? *See page 132.*

_____

_____

12. What can I do today to begin preparing for this job?

_____

_____

13. What classes must I take in high school to qualify for this job?

_____

_____

14. Where in this town or state could I find a job in this field?

_____

15. How does this career mesh with my family plans? Is it consistent with my desired lifestyle? *See page 130.* Does it offer opportunities for flexible hours or part-time work? Is the income high enough so I could maintain my family on it alone if necessary? Could I afford the kind of day care I'd like for my children?

_____

_____

_____

16. Are there opportunities for self-employment in this field (free-lance work, consulting, and the like)?

_____

_____

JOB TITLE _____

1. What specific tasks would I perform on this job? (For example, a salesclerk would answer questions, tidy displays, unpack merchandise, write sales slips, make change, and so on.)

_____

_____

2. What is the job environment likely to be? Is this compatible with the setting I said I wanted on *page 126*?

_____

_____

3. What would be the rewards of working at this job? Are they the same as the ones I listed on *page 129*?

_____

_____

4. I would find this job particularly satisfying because: (Review your passions, values, interests, and life goals for guidance.) *See page 27.*

_____

_____

5. Is this job compatible with my work behavioral style? If so, in what ways? (Don't feel obliged to answer this question unless you have been able to take the complete Personal Profile System.)

_____

_____

6. How much training or education would I need? Where could I get it? Am I willing to make this kind of commitment? *Review pages 116 – 120.*

_____

_____

7. Does this job require specific physical attributes or abilities (strength or health requirements, 20/20 vision, and so on)? If so, what are they? Do I meet them?

_____

_____

8. What could I expect to earn as a beginner in this field? _____

What is the average mid-career salary? _____

9. Does this meet my salary requirements? *See pages 91 and 131.*   Yes   No

_____

10. What is the projected outlook for this career? Will there be many job openings when I am ready to go to work?

_____

_____

155

11. What aptitudes, strengths, and talents does this job call for? Do I have them? Can I get them? *See page 132.*

_____

_____

12. What can I do today to begin preparing for this job?

_____

_____

13. What classes must I take in high school to qualify for this job?

_____

_____

14. Where in this town or state could I find a job in this field?

_____

15. How does this career mesh with my family plans? Is it consistent with my desired lifestyle? *See page 130.* Does it offer opportunities for flexible hours or part-time work? Is the income high enough so I could maintain my family on it alone if necessary? Could I afford the kind of day care I'd like for my children?

_____

_____

_____

16. Are there opportunities for self-employment in this field (free-lance work, consulting, and the like)?

_____

_____

SEEING IN THE MIND'S EYE

156

Picture yourself on the job. What would a typical working day be like? Use the information you gathered in step one to answer the following questions. Sit down, close your eyes, and actually *see* yourself going through the day. Pay particular attention to your feelings. Concern yourself with more than just the work. How would you feel in the morning as you got ready to leave home? What would you do at lunch? How would you feel at the end of the day? How would you spend your evening?

If your working hours would be something other than 9:00 A.M. to 5:00 P.M., adjust the following schedule accordingly.

7:00 A.M. Getting ready for work. What would you wear? How do you feel about going to work? Are you looking forward to the day? _____

_____

8:00 A.M. Traveling to work. How would you get there? How far would you travel? Or would you work at home? _____

_____

9:00 A.M. Walking into work. Describe the setting. Who else is there? What kind of greeting do you get from them? _____

_____

9:00 A.M. to 12:00 noon. What would you be doing during this time? If this is a typical day, what tasks and responsibilities would you carry out?

_____

10:00 A.M. _____

11:00 A.M. _____

Noon. Where would you have lunch, and with whom? Would you socialize with co-workers? Clients?

_____

_____

1:00 P.M. to 5:00 P.M. As the day goes on, see yourself handling some special problems or challenges that might arise in this field. What are they? How do you deal with them? _____

_____

1:00 P.M. _____

2:00 P.M. _____

3:00 P.M. _____

4:00 P.M. _____

5:00 P.M. _____

6:00 P.M. Going home. How do you feel at the end of the day? What might you be thinking about? _____

_____

7:00 P.M. and on. How would you spend a typical evening? Would you need to bring work home? Would you be with your family? Your friends? Are there hobbies or volunteer activities you would want to pursue?

_____

_____

The Shadow Program

Below write a letter to someone you'd like to shadow

STEP THREE

Practice your skill at recognizing entry-level jobs by thinking of possible positions for people interested in the following careers. In column A, list paying jobs that will expose you to the work of each career.

Example: Mechanic = gas jockey, auto parts sales, or cashier

CAREER	COLUMN A PAID	COLUMN B VOLUNTEER
Attorney		
Social worker		
Accountant		
Veterinarian		
Police officer		
Retail salesperson		
Classical musician		
Politician		
Hairstylist		
Office manager		

In column B, list volunteer jobs you could do that would put you in contact with an interesting career possibility.

The Chemistry Test

Ellen's preferred behavior style is dominance. She is a high-energy individual who likes to be in charge of what she is doing. She is decisive and always looks for the most efficient way to do things. She likes to solve problems, is comfortable with change, and is very goal directed.

Robert's style is influencing. He is a creative person who likes flexibility in his work environment. He is gregarious and likes to work with people. Robert's enthusiasm can be contagious. He is good at persuading people to act. He likes varied tasks and will take calculated risks.

Michiko is most comfortable with steadiness. She likes to work with other people, particularly in a supportive role. A patient and considerate person, Michiko likes tasks with well-defined procedures. A steady worker, she follows her projects through from beginning to end. She is a listener and a doer.

Romero's preferred style is compliance. He is extremely detail oriented and is likely to question the decisions of others. He wants to know the facts behind the issues. A conscientious worker, he is precise in any task he undertakes and wants to make sure it is done accurately.

How would you assign the following jobs to these four individuals?

Example: In a book publishing company, jobs would be assigned as follows:

BOOK PUBLISHING
Publisher: *Ellen*

Sales rep: *Robert*

Book designer: *Michiko*

Editor: *Romero*

CONSTRUCTION
Draftsperon _____

Contractor _____

Architect _____

Carpenter _____

HOSPITAL
Minister/priest/rabbi _____

Administrator _____

Lab technician _____

Physician _____

FACTORY
Cafeteria chef _____

Assembly line worker _____

Foreman _____

Quality control inspector _____

SCHOOL
Secretary _____

Principal _____

Attendance clerk _____

Counselor _____

BANK
Loan officer _____

Bank teller _____

Manager _____

Accountant _____

RESEARCH LAB
Project manager _____

Fund raiser _____

Scientist _____

Computer programmer _____

Can you identify which personality type would likely be happiest in each of the jobs below?

PHYSICIAN

Anesthesiologist _____

Surgeon _____

Chief of physicians at local hospital _____

Teacher at medical school _____

TEACHER

Teacher in public school system _____

Private tutor or coach _____

Professor of accounting at university level _____

Trainer for major corporation _____

CHEF

Head chef in a large restaurant — tastes everything! _____

Catering company owner _____

Teacher of adult education cooking classes _____

Associate chef in a restaurant _____

Which career seems to be your favorite choice at this point in time?   What work behavior style do you think would be prominent in someone happy with this job?

_____

Why? _____

_____

Does this match your personal work style? Review your answers on page 42.

Review your answers on page 42.

Yes   No   Perhaps

In what ways? _____

_____

Vocabulary List

alma mater _____

automatic _____

issue _____

logical _____

evaluate _____

differentiate _____

essential _____

gratification _____

long-term _____

pro _____

con _____

probability _____

analyze _____

apprenticeship _____

certification _____

expedite _____

agonize _____

fret _____

avoidance _____

tendency _____

Identifying Choices

List Joyce's goals below.

1. _____

2. _____

Which would you say is her long-term goal? Which is her short-term goal?

What is Joyce's long-term goal? _____

What are the choices she must choose from now that will affect her long-term goal?

1. _____

2. _____

3. _____

Gathering Information

Can you list some other information that would be helpful to Joyce as she weighs her alternatives?

1. _____

2. _____

3. _____

4. _____

Evaluating Choices

Joyce began evaluating her choices on the chart below. In the spaces remaining on the chart, evaluate Joyce's other choice — not to work at all so she can concentrate on her studies.

72

Identify your choices	Pros	Cons	Probability of success
Not work at all	_____	_____	_____
	_____	_____	_____

JESSICA'S STORY

Use the chart below to identify Jessica's choices and evaluate each one.

173

Identify your choices	Pros	Cons	Probability of success
1. _____	_____	_____	_____
_____	_____	_____	_____
2. _____	_____	_____	_____
_____	_____	_____	_____
3. _____	_____	_____	_____
_____	_____	_____	_____
4. _____	_____	_____	_____
_____	_____	_____	_____

If you were Jessica, what would you do? _____

_____

_____

portion of this book may be photocopied or reproduced electronically without written permission from the publisher.

81

JOHN'S STORY

Use the chart below to identify John's choices and evaluate each one.

Identify your choices	Pros	Cons	Probability of success
1. _____	_____	_____	_____
_____	_____	_____	_____
2. _____	_____	_____	_____
_____	_____	_____	_____
3. _____	_____	_____	_____
_____	_____	_____	_____
4. _____	_____	_____	_____
_____	_____	_____	_____

If you were John, what would you do? _____

_____

_____

GLORIA'S CHART

What choice would you make if you were Gloria? _____

_____

Complete the chart below for yourself. Identify and evaluate four possible career choices.

Goal: To identify a career that I will find satisfying.

Decision to be made: Which career would I find most satisfying.

My resources: _____

_____

_____

_____

My wants and needs: _____

_____

_____

_____

Identify your choices	Pros	Cons	Probability of success
1. _____ _____	_____ _____	_____ _____	_____ _____
2. _____ _____	_____ _____	_____ _____	_____ _____
3. _____ _____	_____ _____	_____ _____	_____ _____
4. _____ _____	_____ _____	_____ _____	_____ _____

Make a choice _____

How realistic is this _____

Make a Decision

What is your decision-making (or avoiding) style? Check the place along the scale below that you think most represents your personality. If the words in the left-hand column describe your behavior, you may tend to avoid making decisions. If your behavior is better described by the words on the right, on the other hand, you may tend to make decisions too quickly. There is no right or wrong spot on the scale. But, by being aware of your tendencies, you may be better able to use them in your best interest.

passive	_____ _____ _____ _____ _____ _____ _____	aggressive
contemplative	_____ _____ _____ _____ _____ _____ _____	impulsive
controlled	_____ _____ _____ _____ _____ _____ _____	free
rational	_____ _____ _____ _____ _____ _____ _____	emotional
easily influenced	_____ _____ _____ _____ _____ _____ _____	self-directed
delaying	_____ _____ _____ _____ _____ _____ _____	expediting
cautious	_____ _____ _____ _____ _____ _____ _____	risk-taking
structured	_____ _____ _____ _____ _____ _____ _____	creative
agonizing	_____ _____ _____ _____ _____ _____ _____	relaxed

Chapter 8

Vocabulary List

opportunities _____

_____

flatter _____

_____

courage _____

_____

reputation _____

_____

motivation _____

_____

technique _____

_____

temporary _____

_____

abstract _____

_____

postpone _____

_____

struggle _____

_____

joyous _____

_____

temptation _____

_____

wishful _____

_____

privy _____

_____

discipline _____

_____

destructive _____

_____

goal _____

_____

objective _____

_____

diagram _____

_____

beliefs _____

_____

Who is responsible for solving Crystal and Sterling's problem?

_____

If they get married right away, what sacrifices might they have to make?

_____

If they wait and get married when they graduate from college what sacrifices will they

have to make? _____

_____

What facts should Crystal and Sterling consider before they make their decision?

_____

_____

What wishful thinking might come into play as they make their decision? How likely is

that to happen? _____

_____

If you were Sterling and Crystal, what would you do? _____

_____

Setting Goals and Objectives

Marta's action plan looked like this:

Goal: To answer my questions about archaeology by March 1.

Objective 1: Read at least one book or four articles on archaeology by January 20.

Objective 2: Interview Ms. Rogers in the science department by January 31.

Objective 3A: Call City College and the Natural History Museum by January 31 to see if there are any archaeologists on staff.

Objective 3B: If so, interview a working archaeologist by February 14.

Objective 4: Research climate and reptile life at the three most appealing field sites by February 21.

Now write and diagram some objectives of your own.

To buy a car in six months.

To save for a trip to _____ after graduation.

To make the _____ team next year.

To earn an A in _____ class.

To be accepted at _____ after graduation.
                        (school)

Goal: _____

    Objectives:

      1. _____

      2. _____

      3. _____

Goal: _____

    Objectives:

      1. _____

      2. _____

      3. _____

Now write some goals and objectives of your own.

Your lifestyle goal: _____

    Objective

    1. _____

    2. _____

    3. _____

Your lifestyle goal: _____

    Objective

    1. _____

    2. _____

    3. _____

Your lifestyle goal: _____

    Objective

    1. _____

    2. _____

    3. _____

Chapter 9

Vocabulary List

detour _____

challenge _____

ironic _____

affliction _____

paraplegic _____

debilitate _____

orator _____

serenity _____

solution _____

median _____

consideration _____

obligation _____

valedictorian _____

ambition _____

evidence _____

obstacle _____

concentration _____

confront _____

confident _____

progressive _____

What's Your Excuse?

- ☐ I'm a woman.
- ☐ I'm a man.
- ☐ I'm black.
- ☐ I'm white.
- ☐ I'm hispanic.
- ☐ I'm Asian.
- ☐ I come from a different culture.
- ☐ I'm rich.
- ☐ I'm poor.
- ☐ I'm too smart.
- ☐ I'm not smart enough.
- ☐ I'm too ugly.
- ☐ I'm too fat.
- ☐ I'm too thin.
- ☐ I'm too short.
- ☐ I'm too tall.
- ☐ I'm blind.
- ☐ I have impaired vision.
- ☐ I'm deaf.
- ☐ I have a hearing loss.
- ☐ I can't speak.
- ☐ I have a speech impediment.
- ☐ I'm a paraplegic.
- ☐ I'm a quadraplegic.

- ☐ I've lost a limb.
- ☐ I have a debilitating disease.
- ☐ I've been treated for emotional problems.
- ☐ I've been persecuted for my beliefs.
- ☐ I've had a serious illness.
- ☐ I'm shy.
- ☐ I'm adopted.
- ☐ I'm an orphan.
- ☐ I come from a single-parent home.
- ☐ I've been abused.
- ☐ I've been in trouble with the law.
- ☐ I'm chemically dependent.
- ☐ I have to take care of a parent or sibling.
- ☐ I have a baby.
- ☐ My family won't let me.
- ☐ My family expects too much of me.
- ☐ No one believes in me.
- ☐ I can't do it because . . .
- ☐ Other _____

199

Do you know of any people in your own community who have overcome handicaps or adversities in their lives? If so, add their names below. These people are all heroes. And they can be inspiring role models.

_____

_____

89

No portion of this book may be photocopied or reproduced on a computer without written permission from the publisher.

Taking Responsibility

Can you think of any excuses you've made recently that implied that something or someone else was responsible for your predicament? Write them below.

1. _____

2. _____

3. _____

Now analyze your own role in those situations and rewrite the statements, this time taking responsibility for the problem.

1. _____

2. _____

3. _____

STARTLING STATEMENT QUIZ

Circle the answer you think most accurately completes each of the following statements.

1. Each year, _____ women aged 15-19 in the United States became pregnant.
   a. 250,000
   b. 500,000
   c. 1 million
   d. 1.6 million

2. About _____ percent of unmarried teen mothers keep their babies.
   a. 15
   b. 40
   c. 65
   d. 95

3. Out of every 10 teen mothers, _____ drop out of high school before graduation.
   a. 2
   b. 3
   c. 5
   d. 7

4. In 1995, one out of _____ families headed by a female lived below the poverty line.
   a. 3
   b. 5
   c. 10
   d. 14

5. In 1994, the overall unemployment rate was 12.5 percent. For high school drop-outs, the rate was _____ percent.
   a. 9.7
   b. 10.5
   c. 21.0
   d. 29.8

6. In March 1994, _____ percent of blacks who did not complete high school were unemployed.
   a. 9.7
   b. 13.8
   c. 18.6
   d. 39.8

7. One in every _____ teens aged 18 and above has not completed high school.
   a. 4
   b. 6
   c. 8
   d. 10

8. In 1995, the median income for full-time workers, 25 years and over, with a bachelor's degree or more was $26,843 for women and $43,322 for men The median income for workers with 1-3 years of high school with no diploma was _____ for women and _____ for men.
   a. $6,897 and $12,777
   b. $8,057 and $15,791
   c. $9,927 and $18,903
   d. $16,461 and $25,394

9. The average life expectancy for alcoholics is _____ years.
   a. 37
   b. 45
   c. 58
   d. 72

10. _____ percent of teens who commit suicide are high on drugs or intoxicated on alcohol at the time.
   a. 10
   b. 16
   c. 31
   d. 47

11. The teenage drug problem in the United States is _____ in Japan.
   a. 5 times greater than
   b. 10 times greater than
   c. the same as
   d. 5 times less than

12. The percentage of students using drugs by the time they are sixth graders has _____ since 1975.
   a. tripled
   b. doubled
   c. remained the same
   d. declined

13. In a study of high school students who use cocaine, _____ percent said their grades had dropped significantly.
   a. 12
   b. 26
   c. 48
   d. 69

NOTE: Because we try to maintain current statistics, the numbers in your workbook may not match the numbers in your textbook. Consider the workbook figures current. To score your quiz, use the same letter (a - d) found on page 202 of *Career Choices*.

Brad and Bart

Who acted impulsively? In what way? _____

_____

Try to imagine what the future holds for Brad and Bart. Describe their lives 15 years later in the space below.

Brad's life: _____

_____

_____

Bart's life: _____

_____

_____

Josie and Juan — Judy and Joe

Which couple acted impulsively? In what way? _____

_____

_____

What could life be like for these two couples in 15 years? Visualize their futures and describe them below.

Josie and Juan's life: _____

_____

_____

_____

_____

Judy and Joe's life: _____

_____

_____

_____

_____

204

205

Sam and Janice

Who acted impulsively? In what way? _____

_____

Describe what you think Sam and Janice's lives might be like 15 years from now.

Sam's life: _____

_____

_____

_____

_____

Janice's life: _____

_____

_____

_____

_____

Is It Worth Staying in School?

You decide. Go back to pages 150-151. What careers did you say you might like? List them below.

_____

Imagine that you quit school before graduation. Could you qualify for any of these jobs without a high school diploma?

Yes   **No**

If so, which ones? _____

If not, you need another plan. Review your personal information chart on page 27, your preferred lifestyle on page 63, your budget requirements on page 92 or your hardship budget on page 96, and your career portrait and priorities on page 134.

Now go through the career search process on pages 150-151 once more. This time, though, make sure that a high school diploma isn't required for the jobs you are investigating.

List three careers that meet your personal requirements but do not require a high school diploma below.

_____

Compare these jobs with the ones you listed at the top of the page. How are they different? Which careers do you think would be more satisfying? Why?

_____

_____

_____

_____

Imagine your life 15 years from now. What do you think it would be like if you take a job from your second list, the one that doesn't require a high school education? Which would you find more satisfying — a career from the first or second list?

_____

_____

_____

The Economics of
Bad Habits

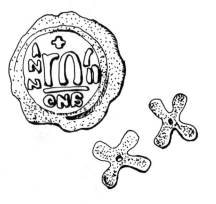

Complete the chart below:

	One pack/day	Other use for money
Cost/year	$	
Cost/10 years	$	
Cost/60 years	$	

Some habits are much more expensive than cigarettes. Before you get involved with them, use the same equation to determine how much they would cost you over a lifetime.

Habit _____

Cost/day _____   Cost/week _____

		Other use for money
Cost/year	$	
Cost/10 years	$	
Cost/60 years	$	

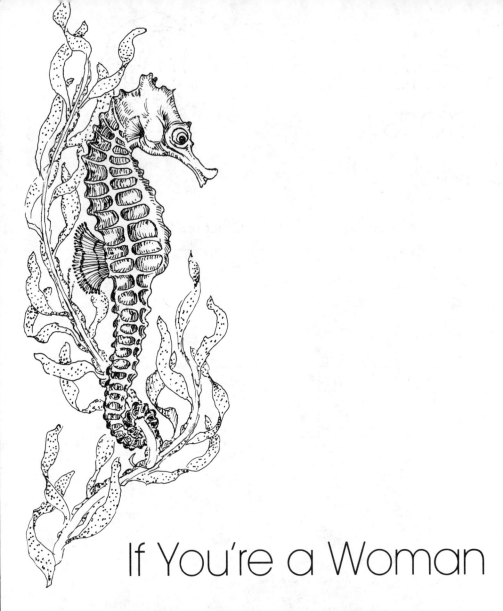

If You're a Woman

Let's explore this concept further. Do you think the workers in each of the careers below are mostly men or mostly women? In the first column beside each job title, write an F if you believe more women work in this field, an M if you think more men do.

Now go back and circle the careers that would probably offer the most flexible hours. In other words, which workers could most easily decide to take time off in the afternoon to attend a son or daughter's basketball game? Some careers are decidedly more flexible than others.

_____	Child care worker	_____	Architect
_____	Receptionist	_____	Auto body repairer
_____	Cashier	_____	Engineer
_____	Janitor	_____	Psychologist (PhD)
_____	Nurse (RN)	_____	Dentist
_____	Plumber	_____	Securities sales rep
_____	Elementary school teacher	_____	Chiropractor

Child care worker	$13,520	Architect	$38,900
Receptionist	$16,016	Auto body repairer	$23,712
Cashier	$11,856	Engineer (mid level)	$54,400
Janitor	$15,236	Psychologist (PhD)	$55,000
Nurse (RN)	$35,464	Dentist	$100,000
Plumber	$27,560	Securities sales rep	$78,000
Elementary school teacher	$36,400	Chiropractor	$75,000

Source: *Occupational Outlook Handbook 1996-97*

Along the bottom of the following graph, first list the careers that are held mostly by women, beginning on the left-hand bottom column (we've already included the child care worker and receptionist as examples). Next add the jobs held mostly by men. Now, star the flexible careers, jobs in which workers can choose their own hours (we've used the chiropractor as an example).

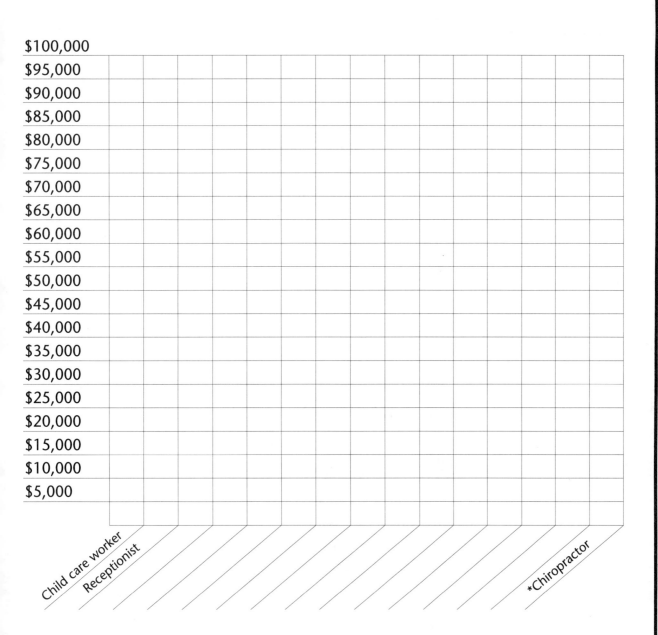

Note: Because we try to maintain current salary figures, the numbers in your workbook may not match the numbers in your textbook. Consider the workbook figures as current.

Now use a pencil to chart the annual average salaries of the flexible careers. Use a pen to chart the annual average salaries of the nonflexible careers. (Note: The salaries we've used come from Department of Labor sources. Individuals might be able to earn a higher salary by working free-lance or starting their own small businesses.)

Suppose a woman with three children suddenly found herself the sole support of her family. A family this size in your community needs at least

$ _____ a year to live in minimal comfort.

Draw a double line across the chart at the $ _____ level.

Which careers from the list would be most suitable for parenting? That is, which would provide both flexibility and an adequate salary? List those careers below. (Hint: These careers are graphed in pencil, above the double line.)

_____

_____

Which of the careers on your list require either a college or vocational degree or some other type of special training? Circle them.

Do more men or women currently hold these jobs?

        More men   More women

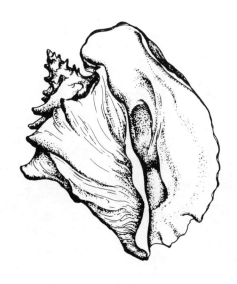

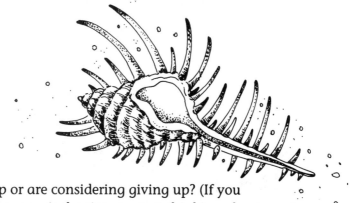

Think of a dream that you have given up or are considering giving up? (If you haven't given your dreams much thought, now is the time to start thinking about them seriously. Try to write them down when they come to mind.)

Before you decide to give up something you once thought you wanted badly, answer the following questions.

What was your old dream? _____

How long did you hold it? _____

When did you decide to give up your dream? _____

Why? _____

What is your new dream? _____

Why does it appeal to you now? _____

Is there hard evidence to support your decision to give up your dream (you can't carry a tune, you've flunked out of school, you've run out of money, and so on)?

_____

If so, is this just an obstacle, or have you really reached the end of the road?

_____

If there is no hard evidence, have you discussed your decision with your teachers or your adviser? What do they think?

_____

If you've come up against an obstacle, would you hang on to your dream if the obstacle would simply disappear (the math requirement is lifted, you win the sweepstakes)?

_____

If you've decided to give up your dream because of some rational obstacle (money, grades), think of as many possible ways to overcome your problem as you can. List them below. Are any of them workable?

_____

_____

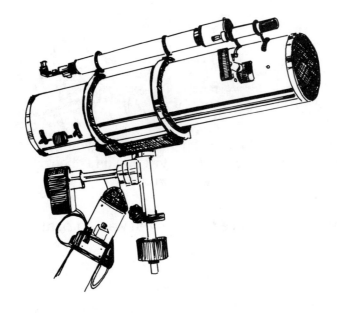

Write a guided visualization that might help you conquer a fear you currently have. Try to see yourself actually doing whatever it is that makes you anxious and write the process below.

_____

_____

_____

_____

_____

_____

_____

_____

_____

_____

_____

_____

_____

_____

Like Sally, you may be facing a number of situations that make you uncomfortable or afraid. Some of them may even tempt you to give up your dream. List five or six fears you have or situations you are avoiding.

_____

_____

_____

_____

_____

Which of these do you think would be easiest for you to overcome? Which would be hardest? List again, starting with the situation that causes you the least anxiety and working toward the item that makes you feel most uncomfortable.

1. _____

2. _____

3. _____

4. _____

5. _____

6. _____

Think of a plan you could use to confront the first two items on your list. Write your plan below. _____

_____

_____

_____

Once you put your plans into action, record your feelings and experiences in the space provided. _____

_____

_____

Write your 10-year plan for Yorik:

Year one:

Education and training: _____

Living arrangements: _____

Employment: _____

Finances: _____

Year three:

Education and training: _____

Living arrangements: _____

Employment: _____

Finances: _____

Year five:

Education and training: _____

Living arrangements: _____

Employment: _____

Finances: _____

Year eight:

Education and training: _____

Living arrangements: _____

Employment: _____

Finances: _____

Year ten:

Education and training: _____

Living arrangements: _____

Employment: _____

Finances: _____

How did Yorik delay gratification in the plan you just described? _____

_____

How might he have acted impulsively? _____

_____

Did he take responsibility for himself?   Yes   No

What excuses might a less determined person have made? _____

_____

What anxieties might Yorik have had to overcome? _____

Chapter 10

Vocabulary List

attitude _____

pretend _____

affirmation _____

effective _____

reverse _____

capable _____

excellence _____

expectation _____

enthusiasm _____

prophecies _____

livelihood _____

enterprise _____

efficient _____

ethic _____

aggression _____

tardy _____

elapse _____

global _____

enormous _____

dignity _____

We've included a few statements as examples. Use them if they could be helpful for you. Then write your own affirmations in the space below. Repeat them to yourself often. Act as if they are true now.

231

I, _____, am confident when meeting new people.

I, _____, am capable of getting a good job.

I, _____, am good at making and keeping friends.

I, _____, _____

I, _____, _____

I, _____, _____

Going For It . . . Work Is an Aggressive Act

236

How aggressive are you when you take on a job? Consider the following situations before you make up your mind.

SCENARIO 1

You are trapped in a burning house. The firefighters arrive, but the doors are locked. Would you prefer to have them

    a. wait patiently for a locksmith (the "nice" thing) or

    b. kick in the doors and windows and get you *out* of there (extremely aggressive behavior)?

SCENARIO 2

You are unjustly accused of a crime. During your trial, your lawyer uncovers evidence that proves your accuser is lying. Should your lawyer

    a. refuse to confront the witness because it wouldn't be polite or

    b. nail him to the wall?

SCENARIO 3

Your car won't start. You need to be at an important conference in an hour. When you call the repair shop, would you rather have the mechanic

    a. sympathize with your plight or

    b. be at your house within 10 minutes and have you on your way in 15?

SCENARIO 4

You are a doctor. You witness a traffic accident in which a child is seriously injured. Should you

    a. try to find out the name of the child's doctor and call him or her or

    b. do what is necessary to save the child's life?

SCENARIO 5

You are one of five junior executives in a small corporation. Each of you is asked to write a proposal for increasing sales. Should you

    a. be careful not to outdo your co-workers or

    b. do your best, for your own sake and the company's?

SCENARIO 6

You are a newspaper reporter who hears a rumor that, if true, could drastically affect the lives of many of your readers. Should you

    a. hope someone will call and tell you what's going on or

    b. investigate vigorously to either verify the story or prove it's not true?

You're the Boss

SHARON

What is Sharon's problem? _____

_____

What advice would you give her during her evaluation?

_____

_____

Write and diagram an objective that Sharon might use to change her behavior.

_____

_____

JACKIE

What is Jackie's problem? _____

What advice would you give her during her evaluation?

_____

_____

Write and diagram an objective that Jackie might use to change her behavior.

_____

_____

DOROTHY

What is Dorothy's problem? _____

What advice would you give her during her evaluation?

_____

_____

Write and diagram an objective that Dorothy might use to change her behavior.

_____

_____

MAT

What is Mat's problem?

_____

_____

_____

What advice would you give him during his evaluation?

_____

_____

_____

Write and diagram an objective that Mat might use to change his behavior.

_____

_____

_____

STUART

What is Stuart's problem?

_____

_____

What advice would you give him during his evaluation?

_____

_____

_____

Write and diagram an objective that Stuart might use to change his behavior.

_____

_____

_____

Now that you've considered some less-than-perfect workers, can you describe a model employee? It might help to review the profiles above. If the characteristics described are undesirable, what opposite traits would make an employee valued by his or her employer?

Employee	Problem	Desired Behavior
Sharon	Tardiness	_____
Jackie	Untruthfulness	_____
Dorothy	Difficult personality	_____
Stuart	Dishonesty	_____
Mat	Laziness	_____

What characteristic did Tim display in each of the situations?

_____

_____

Describe the characteristics of people you would like to hire for your business.

_____

_____

The Employee of the Twenty-first Century

How well will you function in this new environment? The following self-evaluation quiz should give you some idea. Select the answer that best describes or comes closest to your feelings.

1. I view computers as:
   - ☐ a. an important tool.
   - ☐ b. a necessary evil.
   - ☐ c. . . .I don't want anything to do with them.

2. If I need to learn a new procedure while working on a computer, I:
   - ☐ a. get out my manual and figure out how to do it.
   - ☐ b. get help from someone who knows what to do.
   - ☐ c. give up — it takes too much time, and I didn't want to do it anyway.

3. I think of technology as:
   - ☐ a. something we all need to know and understand.
   - ☐ b. . . .I don't think about it much.
   - ☐ c. unnecessary — I don't need these new gadgets.

4. When I get my diploma at graduation, I'll probably think:
   - ☐ a. this is really just the beginning of my education.
   - ☐ b. about what I'm going to do now.
   - ☐ c. thank goodness, no more school.

5. When I have a question about something, I:
   - ☐ a. look up the answer or call someone who should know.
   - ☐ b. make a mental note to keep my eyes open for the answer.
   - ☐ c. forget about it — it probably wasn't important anyway.

6. I think of change:
   - ☐ a. as an opportunity.
   - ☐ b. with caution.
   - ☐ c. with resistance.

7. If, halfway through a project, it becomes apparent that my plan for completing it won't work, I would:
   - ☐ a. rethink my plan and come up with a better one.
   - ☐ b. worry about the project and hope to come up with a better plan someday.
   - ☐ c. lose interest and scrap the project.

8. When I'm around people from other cultures:
   - ☐ a. I appreciate their diversity.
   - ☐ b. I'm curious — but cautious.
   - ☐ c. . . .I am uncomfortable with people who are not like me.

9. The idea of traveling to other countries:
   - ☐ a. sounds exciting to me.
   - ☐ b. is of some interest to me.
   - ☐ c. does not interest me at all.

10. Learning at least one other language:
    - ☐ a. is important for everyone.
    - ☐ b. is probably a good idea.
    - ☐ c. is unnecessary — I can get by speaking only English.

To score your self-evaluation, go back and give yourself 3 points for every "a" answer you checked, 2 points for every "b" and 1 point for every "c." If your total score is 20–30, you have the attitudes that will make you a valued employee in the twenty-first century. They include the following.

Your objectives:

Technology:
1. _____

2. _____

Love of learning:
1. _____

2. _____

Flexibility:
1. _____

2. _____

International perspective:
1. _____

2. _____

Chapter 11

Vocabulary List

principles _____

publication _____

resume _____

summary _____

original _____

chronological _____

honesty _____

references _____

draft _____

polite _____

impression _____

vaccination _____

misdemeanor _____

felony _____

appropriate _____

rejection _____

mentor _____

inspirational _____

tragedy _____

negotiable _____

Use this page to write a draft of a resume for yourself.

Job Applications

Some forms ask for information you may not know offhand. Ask your parents for help if you don't remember any of the following:

Your mother's maiden (unmarried) name _____

Previous addresses if you've moved in recent years _____

Illnesses or health problems you've had _____

Dates of your last physical and/or vaccinations _____

Some other questions you should be prepared to answer include the following:

Do you have the legal right to work in the United States? (If you are a U.S. citizen or have a work visa, answer yes.)   Yes   No

How will you get to and from work? _____

When are you available to work (days and hours)? _____

How many hours per week do you wan't to work? _____

What salary do you expect? _____

Have you served in the military?   Yes   No

Have you ever been convicted of a misdemeanor or felony?   Yes   No

Most forms ask you to sign and date your application before you turn it in to the employer. Your signature indicates that the information you have provided is true and complete. It also gives the employer the right to contact schools, former employers, or references to verify your answers.

The Job Interview

You might be asked some or all of the following questions. Write your answers here:

Why do you think you would be good at this job? _____

_____

How did you hear about this company? _____

Why do you want to work here? _____

_____

What classes are you taking in school? _____

_____

What is your favorite class? _____

What is your grade point average? _____

What are your strengths? _____

_____

What are your weaknesses? _____

_____

What are your hobbies? _____

What are your plans for the future? _____

_____

When would you be able to start working here? _____

How many hours per week could you work? _____

How would you get to and from work? _____

What salary would you need to earn? _____

Is there anything you'd like to ask me about the job? _____

_____

Making Connections

Can you think of people who have served as mentors for you in the past? List them below. What did they do that you found helpful?

_____

_____

_____

_____

How about now? Are there potential or actual mentors in your life? List them here. How have they, or how could they, help you?

_____

_____

_____

_____

Think about the training or work you are currently planning to get or do in the next 10 years. What kinds of mentors do you need? List them by title or classification below.

_____

_____

_____

_____

Have you ever been a mentor? To whom? What did you do? How did you feel about it?

_____

_____

_____

_____

Vocabulary List

overwhelming _____

alternative _____

misfortune _____

alienate _____

despotism _____

solace _____

chastens _____

virtue _____

duration _____

perspective _____

patience _____

surmount _____

muff _____

fantasies _____

impress _____

genius _____

niche _____

respect _____

appreciation _____

success _____

Where is it You Want to Go?

On page 177 you indicated the career for which you want to prepare. Write that job title in the space below.

_____

How much education and/or training will you need to complete before you can get an entry-level job in this field (from pages 150-153)?

TRAINING	DURATION
_____	_____
_____	_____
_____	_____
_____	
	Total _____

Use the information above to determine how many more years of formal education or training you need. Enter that number below.

_____ years

What educational requirements must you meet during each of those years (classes you need to take, grades you must maintain, and so forth)? List them on the following chart.

HIGH SCHOOL
This year:

_____   _____

_____   _____

Next year:

_____   _____

_____   _____

The year after:

_____   _____

_____   _____

And on . . .

_____   _____

_____   _____

POST-HIGH SCHOOL
Year one:

_____   _____

_____   _____

Year two:

_____   _____

_____   _____

Year three:

_____   _____

_____   _____

Year four:

_____   _____

_____   _____

Year five:

_____   _____

_____   _____

Year six:

_____   _____

_____   _____

Year seven:

_____   _____

_____   _____

And on . . .

271

We have redesigned the chart to give you room to expand on your plans for the next 10-15 years. On each line write your major activity, type of education, or work for that year.

273

90	_____
80	_____
70	_____
60	_____
50	_____
45	_____
40	_____
35	_____
30	_____
29	_____
28	_____
27	_____
26	_____
25	_____
24	_____
23	_____
22	_____
21	_____
20	_____
19	_____
18	_____
17	_____
16	_____
15	_____
10	_____
0	_____

Delaying Gratification

274

Following a plan necessarily means delaying gratification. Turn to page 183 to review this concept. Admittedly, that's not always easy to do. It helps, though, if you are motivated and prepared. Answering the following questions should help you be both.

Can you think of sacrifices you might need to make in order to achieve your goal? Might you need to give up some social activities, for example? Will you have to spend some of the money you now use for clothes or recreation for tuition? List them below.

_____

_____

_____

_____

What commitments are you *willing to make*? (Will you study for a certain amount of time every day? Will you take a job to earn money for school?)

_____

_____

_____

List the rewards you hope to gain from those commitments and sacrifices below.

275

_____

_____

_____

Do the rewards make the sacrifices and commitments seem worthwhile?

_____

_____

_____

Jodie's example: What do I want? *I want to be a lawyer.*

What are my choices right now? *To register for the advanced math class that will help me get into law school, or to take the art class that would be more fun.*

I want to *be a lawyer,* **therefore I will** *take the math class.*

What do I want? _____

What are my choices right now? _____

_____

_____

I want to _____ **therefore I will** _____

Facing Fears and Anxieties

In the space below, anticipate your fears by listing every excuse you can think of for giving up your dream.

_____

_____

_____

Now list every reason or excuse you can think of for not successfully completing the preparation or training you need to have the career you want.

_____

_____

_____

Now that you've faced your fears, take responsibility for them. For each excuse listed above, write an affirmation that counters the fear and gives you power. (See chapter 10.)

_____

_____

_____

_____

_____

_____

Just as you are responsible for overcoming your own fears, you must take responsibility for solving you own problems. Can you think of any roadblocks or detours that might get in the way of your success during the next 10 years? (Review pages 203–215.) List those possibilities below.

1. _____

2. _____

3. _____

4. _____

Imagine your life 15 years from now. What will it be like if one of these events actually occurs?

_____

_____

_____

_____

_____

Remember that you are in control of the situation. Can you think of things you can do now to avoid these problems? Write a goal and two objectives that will help you do that in the space below.

GOAL: _____

    Objective: _____

    _____

    Objective: _____

    _____

Your Plan

On the following pages, you will write a detailed action plan for the next 10 years. Before you begin, sit down and visualize your life over this period of time. (See page 217 on visualizations.) How old will you be in 10 years? What do you think you'll look like? How do you want to feel about yourself and about your life?

Your 10-Year Goal: _____

_____

Once you have a clear picture of where you'd like to go and how you might get there, write your plans below. Word them as measurable objectives if you can.

YEAR ONE — (Next year)

Education and training: _____

Living arrangements: _____

Employment: _____

Finances: _____

YEAR TWO

Education and training: _____

Living arrangements: _____

Employment: _____

Finances: _____

YEAR THREE

Education and training: _____

Living arrangements: _____

Employment: _____

Finances: _____

YEAR FOUR

Education and training: _____

Living arrangements: _____

Employment: _____

Finances: _____

YEAR FIVE

Education and training: _____

Living arrangements: _____

Employment: _____

Finances: _____

YEAR SIX

Education and training: _____

Living arrangements: _____

Employment: _____

Finances: _____

YEAR SEVEN

Education and training: _____

Living arrangements: _____

Employment: _____

Finances: _____

YEAR EIGHT

Education and training: _____

Living arrangements: _____

Employment: _____

Finances: _____

YEAR NINE

Education and training: _____

Living arrangements: _____

Employment: _____

Finances: _____

YEAR TEN

Education and training: _____

Living arrangements: _____

Employment: _____

Finances: _____

281

It's one thing to be responsible for your own actions, but quite another to feel you have to do everything on your own. Part of responsibility is knowing when to get help and where to get it. Review page 262 on the importance of mentors. Can you think of people in your life right now who could be of assistance in reaching your goals? If so, list them below. If not, start watching for these important people to turn up in your life. Whether or not you know any now, you are sure to meet others in the next few years. Learn to recognize them, and be open to the things they have to teach you.

_____

_____

_____

_____

282

Back on page 61 you stated your mission in life. Is it still the same? Restate or rewrite it below and refer to it often. Although your mission may change, it will keep you on course. In the end, you are likely to judge your own success or failure according to how well you have lived up to this purpose.

_____

_____

_____

_____

Congratulations on the completion of your *Workbook*!

If you would like your own copy of *Career Choices*, you may purchase a copy through your local bookstore. If the store does not have it in stock, ask the salesperson to order it. You may also write to Academic Innovations, 3463 State Street, Suite 267, Santa Barbara, CA 93105 or call (805) 967-8015 for ordering information.

Portfolio

Homework Assignments

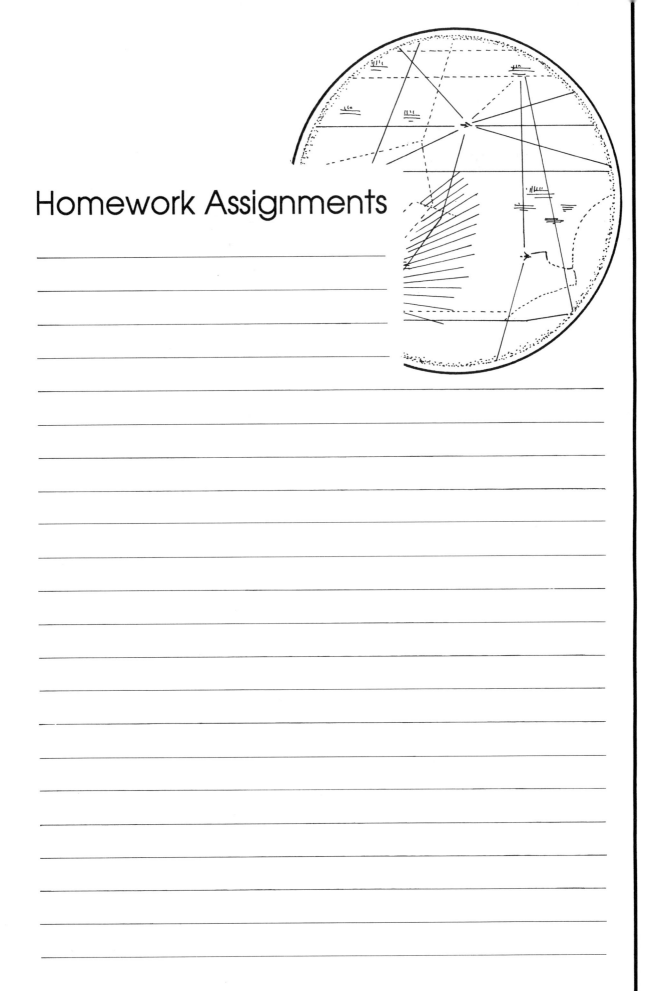

_____

_____

_____

_____

_____

_____

_____

_____

_____

_____

_____

_____

_____

_____

_____

_____

_____

_____

_____

_____

_____

_____

Homework Assignments

Grades

Notes